LEAVING CERTI

RAPID REVISION

AGRICULTURAL SCIENCE

Elaine Buckley Murphy

Folens

Editor

Alastair Hall

Layout

Oisin Burke

Cover

Karen Hoey

Artwork

Michael Phillips, Gary Dermody and Steph Dix of Graham Cameron Illustration

© Elaine Buckley Murphy 2008

Folens Publishers,

Hibernian Industrial Estate,

Greenhills Road,

Tallaght,

Dublin 24.

ISBN 978 1 84741 162 4

Produced in Ireland by Folens Publishers

Contents

Acknowledgments

I would like to thank everyone at Folens, especially John O'Connor, Ciara McNee and Alastair Hall for their advice, time and patience.

Thanks to all my students in Bruce College, Cork for their constant inspiration.

I would also like to thank Pat, Carmel, Danny and Angela Buckley (from Caherbarnagh), the Murphy family (from Pluckanes) especially Denis for answering all my questions, Elizabeth Spillane, John Barrett and Emma Cooper for their help, support and encouragement during the writing of this book.

Finally, I would like to say a special thank you to my husband John.

Animal production

The types of animal production dealt with in the agricultural science course are dairy, beef, sheep, pig and poultry.

The aim in animal production is to ensure that all animals reach their full potential, e.g. dairy cows produce the maximum amount of milk, beef animals produce the best quality meat, etc.

A high level of management is required for these targets to be met.

Feeding the pregnant ewe/cow

Steaming up

Steaming up is the term used to describe feeding a pregnant animal good-quality silage and concentrates containing 15 per cent crude protein.

* Cows should receive 2 kg per day of concentrates for 10 weeks before calving and 6 kg per day at calving.

* The amount of concentrates fed to ewes should increase gradually up to 0.5 kg per day for ewes carrying singles and up to 0.7 kg per day for ewes carrying twins.

Advantages of steaming up

Steaming up is very important in animal production, as 75 per cent of the calf/lamb develops in the last few weeks of pregnancy.

Steaming up helps:

✓ To ensure a strong healthy calf/lamb is born.
✓ To get the cow/ewe into full milk production in the new lactation.
✓ The development of the udder.
✓ To ensure the cow/ewe has enough energy to give birth.
✓ To ensure the cow has enough energy to 'milk off her back' (*see* page 5).
✓ To prevent pregnancy toxaemia (also known as twin lamb disease) in ewes.

Care of the newborn lamb/calf

Management of the newborn lamb/calf

1. Mucus is removed from the nose and mouth of the young animal.

2. The lamb/calf is licked dry by the mother or dried using straw.

3. The navel is treated with iodine.

4. The lamb/calf suckles its mother to receive colostrum and then milk.

5. The lamb/calf is vaccinated.

6. The lamb/calf is fed hay and concentrates for the development of rumen.

Fig. 1.1 A tagged calf.

> **PURPOSE OF TAGGING ANIMALS**
> * Tracing.
> * Identification.
> * Keeping records.
> * Legal requirement.

Reasons young animals are fed colostrum

* Colostrum provides antibodies to build up the immune system.

* It contains minerals and vitamins to stimulate growth and build up the immune system.

* It has a laxative effect which cleans out the sticky black substance lining the digestive system.

* It is a suitable food while rumen is developing.

* It increases the body temperature of the young animal.

The feeding principles of newly born calves

* Calves are first fed colostrum. They are then fed milk or milk replacer.

* The calves have access to hay and concentrates to develop their rumen.

* In dairy production, calves should graze fresh, leafy grass in a **leader–follower** grazing system (*see* page 50).

* Creep grazing and creep feeding should be employed in sheep and suckler beef production.

Fig. 1.2 A creep feeder used in lamb production.

The replacement heifer

Replacement heifers are required to replace dairy cows that are removed from the herd. These cows may have been removed for a number of reasons.

(*See* 'Reasons why animals may be culled from the herd/flock', page 15.)

Breeding policy for the replacement heifers

* Heifers are born in January/February.
* Select heifers from high milk-producing cows.
* Heifers come into heat at 8–12 months, but are not put in calf.
* They are mated at 15 months and 300 kg.
* Use a suitable breed of bull, usually Aberdeen Angus.
* Heifers are due to calve in January/February of second year.

Why the replacement heifer should be 300 kg at mating

Replacement heifers should be 300 kg at mating because this ensures that:

* The animals are mature enough for mating.
* They are mature enough for calving.
* They can meet the calving deadline, i.e. calve at 2 years.
* They have the potential of producing a high milk yield.
* Their reproductive organs are properly developed.

GROWTH TARGETS FOR THE REPLACEMENT HEIFER	
YEAR 1	
January/February	Calf ⟹ 40 kg.
April	Turn out to grass ⟹ 72 kg.
November	At housing ⟹ 200 kg. (Fed good-quality silage and concentrates over the winter.)
YEAR 2	
April/May	Turn out to grass ⟹ 300 kg. (Heifer is put in calf – cows calve at 2 years of age.)
November	At housing ⟹ 450 kg. (Steaming up is caried out during the winter.)
January/February	500 kg before calving.

Replacement heifers have to be fed for growth, maintenance and production during their first lactation.

The dairy cow

Reducing the mortality of cows at calving

* Choose a suitable breed of bull.
* Keep records of when the cow was inseminated.
* Carry out steaming up.
* Ensure the cow is in good condition prior to calving.

* Isolate the cow 1–2 days before calving.

* Inspect the animal regularly.

* Have an experienced person at hand (usually the farmer).

* Assist the birth if necessary.

* Call the vet if difficulties arise.

* First time calvers and cows crossed with large continental breeds should have their amount of feed reduced before calving.

Why the cow loses weight for a period of time after calving

* The cow used energy to carry the unborn calf.

* The cow used energy giving birth.

* After calving, the energy required to produce the colostrum/milk grows faster than the increase in the cow's feed intake resulting in an energy deficit.

* To compensate for the deficit, the cow will breakdown available body reserves during this period. This is known as 'milking off her back'.

Management of the cow in early lactation

* After calving, the cow is fed good-quality silage and concentrates.

* The cow is put out to grass as soon as it becomes available.

* A proper grazing regime is employed – strip or paddock grazing.

* The cow needs to be given sufficient nutrients in order to reach her lactation peak.

* The peak governs total milk yield for the lactation.

* The cow needs to be fed for maintenance and production.

* First time calvers require extra feed because they also need to be fed for growth.

* Older cows also require extra feeding.

* The cow is given Cal – Mag to prevent milk fever and grass tetany.

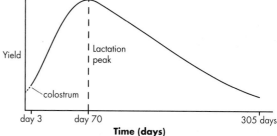

Fig. 1.3 The lactation curve.

The let down process

Milk is produced in the glandular tissue of the udder. Glandular tissue is made up of alveoli cells.

1. When the udder of the cow is washed prior to milking, nerve impulses send a message to the brain.

2. The pituitary gland in the brain then releases the hormone oxytocin into the bloodstream.

3. Oxytocin causes the muscles around the alveoli to contract, forcing the milk out into the teat cisterns.

4. The action of this hormone lasts between 3 and 7 minutes and therefore it is important for milking to be started immediately after stimulating the udder.

Management of the cow in mid and late lactation

At this stage, the lactation peak has been reached and the cow's milk yield is declining. The cow is now able to maintain itself on good quality grass and does not need to be fed any concentrates. In late lactation, daily yields become so small that the cow is only milked once a day. When the cow is dried off, it is given medication in the form of drying-off tubes to prevent mastitis. The cow is dried off two months before calving.

Why cows require a rest period between lactations

* The milk secretory cells need time to regenerate.
* The cow needs time to recover its body condition prior to the new milking season.
* It enables the cow to produce good quality colostrum for the newborn calf.
* The calf's demands increase towards the end of gestation.
* It allows time for steaming up to be employed.

Improving production in the dairy herd

* Use suitable breeds.
* Employ a suitable breeding programme.
* Use artificial insemination or top bulls.
* Replace cows with heifers that are produced by cows with good characteristics.
* Carry out stripping milk and milk recording.
* Cull poor-performing animals.

* Feed the cow high quality foods.

* Maintain good hygiene in the milking parlour.

> **DUAL PURPOSE BREED**
> Cattle that have good dairy and beef characteristics, e.g. Friesians.

Fig. 1.4 The Friesian cow.

Factors which affect the composition of cow's milk

* The age of the cow.
* The quality of the feed.
* The stage in lactation.
* The breed of the cow.
* The time of year.
* The time of milking (morning or evening).
* A higher somatic cell count in older animals.

Advantages and disadvantage of milking cows more than twice a day

✓ Overall increase in milk yield.

✓ Empties the udder and stimulates the alveoli cells to start secreting milk again.

❖ Extremely time consuming and would not be economically feasible for the farmer.

Fig. 1.5 A rotary milking parlour.

Factors involved in ensuring proper hygiene in the milking parlour

* Wash the udder and teats of the cow prior to milking.

* Wash the clusters, milk line and cooler on a regular basis.

* Use a filter in the milking machine to remove any dirt particles which may get into the milk.

* Wash the bulk tank regularly.

The bodily characteristics of dairy animals

* Wedge-shaped animals.

* Topline and underline converge at a point beyond the head.

* Narrow shoulders and wide hindquarters.

* Long and narrow head.

* Long and thin neck.

* Shoulder blades are close together.

* Strong shoulders but not well-fleshed.

* Level back.

* Wide legs and hindquarters; strong but not well-fleshed.

Beef farming

OUTLINE OF A TWO YEAR CALF TO BEEF SYSTEM	
First summer	• Calf should be about 80 kg. • Leader–follower system of grazing. • Protect against diseases.

First winter	• Calf should be about 200 kg. • House in open sheds or slatted units. • Feed high quality silage. • Protect against diseases.
Second summer	• Calf should be about 280 kg. • Second in line in the leader–follower system. • Dose for lice, stomach worms, lungworms, etc.
Second winter	• Calf should be about 450 kg. • Feed good quality silage and concentrates. • Reaches slaughter weight at the end of the second winter.

> **SLAUGHTER WEIGHT VARIES WITH BREED**
> • Aberdeen Angus: 450 kg.
> • Continental beef breed: 850 kg.

Compensatory growth in beef animals

Compensatory growth is the increase in growth that occurs when animals are fed well after a period of restricted feeding. In beef farming, compensatory growth is a method of keeping down winter feeding costs.

1. Over the winter, animals are only fed silage – fed for maintenance only. During this period, their frame grows but they put on little meat; this is known as a store period.

2. The following spring, they experience an increased growth rate when put out to grass.

Grading beef animals at slaughter

* The EUROP grading system is used.

* Animals are graded on the basis of conformation and fatness.

* Conformation grades range from E to P.

* E is the best conformation and P is the worst conformation.

* Fatness grades range from 1 to 5.

* One (1) is the leanest and 5 is the fattest.

	E	U	R	O	P
1	░	░			
2	░	░			
3					
4^L					
4^H					
5					

> For animals **to achieve the best grading**, i.e. the shaded area, use continental beef breeds and feed them a high plane of nutrition.

Table 1.1 The EUROP grading system.

Fig. 1.6 A beef heifer approaching slaughter weight.

Feeding programme for suckler beef cows

* The cow needs only to be fed for maintenance for 5–6 months of the year. This maintenance feeding keeps down feeding costs and therefore increases the profit margins.

* For the remaining 6–7 months of the year, the cow needs to be fed a high plane of nutrition. There are three reasons for the cow being fed a high plane of nutrition:

  ➤ Steaming up prior to calving.

  ➤ Good milk production to feed the newborn calf.

  ➤ To ensure a correct condition score at mating.

* The calf suckles the cow from birth to weaning at housing.
* Good quality grazing can supply all the cow's nutritional needs.
* Concentrates are usually fed just before and after calving.

The bodily characteristics of beef animals

* Block-like animals.
* Topline and underline are parallel.
* Wide shoulders and hindquarters and well-fleshed.
* Short and wide head.
* Short and thick neck.
* Shoulder blades are well apart and well-fleshed.
* Level back; broad at all points.
* Wide legs and hindquarters and evenly fleshed.

Sheep farming

OUTLINE OF THE YEAR IN LOWLAND SHEEP PRODUCTION	
January/February	• Lambing takes place.
March/April/May	• The lamb suckles its mother. • Creep feeding and creep grazing are introduced. • The lamb is weaned at 14 weeks or sold as early lamb.
June/July/August	• The lamb grazes good quality grass. • The lamb is sold as it reaches slaughter weight. • The ewe is put on poor quality pasture prior to flushing.
September/October	• The ewe is put on good quality pasture for flushing. • Mating occurs. • The ewe remains on good quality pasture after mating.
November/December	• The ewe is fed for maintenance only.
December/January	• Steaming up occurs prior to lambing.

Fig. 1.7 Lambs approaching slaughter weight.

The breeding strategy employed in lowland sheep production

This involves the production of lambs for slaughter.

* The rams are chosen to give fast growth rate and good carcass quality, e.g. Suffolk or Texel rams.

* The rams are mated with crossbred ewes.

* The reproductive efficiency target is to sell 200 lambs per 100 ewes mated.

Factors influencing wool quality

* The animal's level of nutrition.

* The breed of the animal.

* The animal's health.

* Time of year the sheep is shorn.

Flushing and its advantages

Flushing involves feeding female animals on a low plane of nutrition after weaning, followed immediately by a high plane of nutrition 3–4 weeks before mating.

This results in:

* More eggs being released at ovulation.

* More regular heat periods.

* Higher conception rate.

* Better implantation.

Flushing is continued for 3–4 weeks after mating.

Looking after the ewe from mating to lambing

* Flushing is continued for a further 3–4 weeks.

* Feeding for maintenance for weeks 5–15.

* Steaming up prior to lambing.

* Lambing should be observed. A vet should be called if difficulties arise.

Synchronised breeding

Synchronised breeding is used to reduce the mating and lambing period to about three weeks. This has the advantage of reducing the farmers work load in the spring and makes flock management easier.

1. Progesterone implanted sponges are placed in the birth canal of the ewe and left there for between 12 and 16 days.

2. All sponges are removed at the same time.

3. Two days later, all ewes come into heat.

The ram:ewe ratio is reduced from 1:40 to 1:10.

Breeding out of season

Breeding out of season is employed to get ewes to produce lambs which will be ready for the Easter market. For this to occur, lambs will have to be born in the month of December, therefore the ewes must be pregnant in July.

1. The ewe is a seasonal breeder and only comes into heat between September and February.

2. Progesterone implanted sponges are placed in the birth canal of the ewe and left there for between 12 and 16 days.

3. All sponges are removed at the same time and the ewe is given an injection of PMSG.

> **PMSG**
> Pregnant Mare Serum Gonadotrophin.

4. Two days later, all ewes come into heat.

The ram:ewe ratio is reduced from 1:40 to 1:10.

What is meant when mountain ewes are 'culled for age', 'draft' or 'cast' ewes?

These terms describe when a mountain ewe is sold to a hill farmer. It is moved from the mountain to the better conditions in hill farming. This results in it producing lambs for several more years than it would if it was left on the mountain.

Housing cattle and sheep

Housing requirements of animals

* Animals must have adequate space.

* Houses must be well-ventilated and draught-free.

* Houses should be insulated in order to retain the heat.

* There should be a proper waste disposal system.

* Clean water should be available.

* Proper bedding should be present.

* Houses should be hygienic.

* Animals should be dosed and vaccinated at housing.

HOUSING BEEF ANIMALS

- **Beef weanlings**
  $1.4 \ m^2$ floor and $7 \ m^3$ of air space per animal.
- **Two year olds**
  $2 \ m^2$ floor and $10 \ m^3$ of air space per animal.

Advantages of housing cattle and sheep over the winter

✓ Prevents a fall in body temperature.

✓ Makes the feeding easier as there is no grass growth over the winter.

✓ Protects the animals from weather extremes.

✓ Prevents poaching.

✓ Eases prevention and identification of diseases.

Why animals are fed concentrates

* Concentrates supplement poor quality fodder crops.

* Farmers are able to control the animal's diet.

* Farmers can ensure animals have a balanced diet.

* Concentrates provide fibre.

* Concentrates ensure production targets are met.

* Concentrates are high in dry matter content.

* Concentrates are a high-energy food.

Fig. 1.8 Concentrates.

Culling animals and choosing their replacements

Reasons why animals may be culled from the herd/flock

* A reduction in prolificacy (litter size).

* A reduction in milk yield.

* A decline in the milk quality.

* Injuries to the feet.

* Damage to the udder.

* Contracting a disease.

* Infertility problems.

* Poor body conformation.

* Old age.

* Bad temperament.

* Difficult to manage.

* Problems giving birth.

* To improve breeding/grading up.

> **GRADING UP**
> The practice of replacing low-yielding cows with heifers from higher-yielding cows in the herd, with the objective of increasing the average milk yield per cow.

Factors to consider when selecting an animal for breeding

* Full set of teeth.
* Healthy feet.
* Properly formed mouth.
* Suitable breed.
* Good pedigree.
* Age.
* Properly formed udder.
* Healthy animal.
* Condition score.
* Suitable conformation.

Points to consider when purchasing animals

* Know the producer.
* Conformation of the animal.
* Check eyes, ears, nose, mouth, navel and anus for any discharges.
* Sound legs and feet.
* Healthy, well-formed udder (if relevant).
* Healthy teeth.

Condition scoring in animals

Condition scoring is the ratio of lean to fat on the animal's body. It is accessed by measuring the amount of fat cover on various parts of the animal's body.

* Condition scores range from 0–5 in cattle and sheep.
* In pigs, condition scores range from 0–9.
* A condition score of zero (0) is an animal that is extremely thin.
* A condition score of 5 (cattle and sheep) or 9 (pigs) represents an animal that has an excessive amount of fat on the body.
* Ideal scores are: cattle/sheep 2.5–3; pigs 4.5–5.

Pig and poultry production

Pig and poultry production are highly intensive. There are two types of production units: integrated and subcontracted units.

1. An **integrated** pig or poultry production unit consist of a breeding and rearing unit and a fattening unit all on the one farm.

2. A **subcontracted** pig or poultry production unit is when there are units located on different farms.

Advantages of an integrated production unit

✓ They are self-contained, which lessens the risk of disease entry.

✓ They eliminate the stress of transportation on the animal.

✓ Farmers are able to select their own breeding stock.

Disadvantages of an integrated production unit

❖ Diseases spread rapidly if they enter the unit.

❖ A very high level of animal management is required.

❖ Slurry storage requirements are increased.

Factors which affect an animal's Food Conversion Ratio (FCR)

Diet, health, management, breed, housing, age and sex.

Advantages of a good FCR

✓ A low FCR means good food efficiency.

✓ Improved feed efficiency means greater profit margins.

	FCRS
Weaners	1.75:1
Fatteners	3.25:1
Poultry	2:1

Outline the characteristics of the main breeds of pigs used in pig production

Landrace – a Danish breed

* Good body conformation – long body, which yields a lot of back bacon and pork.
* Good meat quality – ham, bacon and pork.

Large White – a British breed

* Fast growth rate.
* High prolificacy.
* Good food conversion ratio.
* Good meat quality.

Hybrid vigour in pig production

Hybrid vigour: A cross between two dissimilar individuals producing an offspring which is superior to either parent.

Hybrid vigour is common practice. Most herds consist of F1 hybrid sows which are then crossed with a pure bred boar.

Care of the newborn bonham

1. The navel is treated with iodine to prevent navel ill.
2. Their front teeth are removed to prevent injury to the sow's teats.
3. Their tails are docked.
4. The males are castrated.
5. An infrared lamp is used to keep the bonhams warm.
6. After 2–3 days, they are given an iron injection to prevent anaemia.
7. The bonhams suckle sow (first colostrum then milk).
8. After 5–7 days, creep ration is scattered on the floor.
9. Water is available.
10. They are weaned abruptly after 5–6 weeks.

The feeding of weaners and fatteners

∗ Feed is available ad lib.

∗ They are fed high-quality weaner/fattener ration.

∗ The weaner/fattener ration has a high protein content (contains lysine – an essential amino acid).

∗ Water is available.

∗ In the case of fatteners, in the weeks prior to slaughter feed is restricted to prevent fat deposition on the carcass.

- **Bonhams** weigh between 1 and 1.5 kg when they are born.
- **Weaners** are between 9 and 32 kg.
- **Fatteners** are between 33 and 80–82 kg.

Housing of pigs

Below are the different houses found on the pig farm.

∗ Farrowing house.

∗ Dry sow house.

∗ Weaner house.

∗ Fattener house.

– Water must be available.

– It must be hygienic.

– It must be maintained at a suitable temperature.

– It must be well-insulated or have low roofs.

– It must be well-ventilated and draught-proof.

– It must have adequate space for the animals.

– Weaners being weaned at the same time are mixed for a short period and then groups of similar-weight pigs are selected.

– These groups are moved to the weaner house and stocked at a high density in order to maintain the temperature of the house at 24 °C.

THE IDEAL TEMPERATURES

- Farrowing house: 20 °C.
- Weaner house: 24 °C.
- Fattener house: 22 °C.

– When weaners are moved to the fattener house, they are again mixed and regrouped to maintain a temperature of 22 °C.

Critical temperature

Critical temperature is defined as the house temperature at which the animal can maintain its body temperature without weight loss or the need for extra food. This results in a good FCR and therefore a greater profit margin.

Replacement gilts

A gilt is a female pig that has not yet had its first litter.

As fatteners approach slaughter weight, the females displaying the best general health and conformation are chosen as replacement gilts. Gilts are moved to the dry sow house and first served at 7 or 8 months when their weight is around 110 kg.

Management of the pregnant sow

1. The sow is housed in the dry sow house.

2. She is fed 2.5 kg of meals once a day.

3. In early pregnancy, she may be given extra concentrates because she may be overly thin after rearing the bonhams of her previous litter.

4. For the final 3–4 weeks, she is fed an extra 0.5 kg of concentrates per day.

5. One week before giving birth, she is moved to the farrowing house.

6. She is washed, deloused and disinfected.

> The **increase in feed** in the last 3–4 weeks ensures the birth of healthy bonhams and good milk production by the sow.

7. She is vaccinated and put into the farrowing crate.

8. The temperature of the farrowing house is maintained at 20 °C.

9. The sow is observed during the birth and assisted if necessary.

10. If problems occur, the vet is called.

Advantages of the farrowing crate

✓ Allows the sow to farrow without causing risk to the bonhams.
✓ Allows her to stand up and lie down without crushing the bonhams.
✓ Allows the bonhams easy access to the sow for suckling.

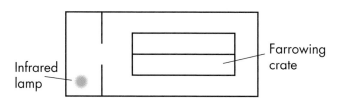

Fig. 1.9 The farrowing house and farrowing crate.

Management of the sow after the birth of the bonhams

1. The sow is left in the farrowing crate.

2. The bonhams suckle their mother for 5–6 weeks.

3. The sow is fed suckling ration at a rate of 1.8 kg per day and an extra 0.5 kg per bonham.

4. A separate supply of water is available.

5. When the bonhams are weaned, the sow is moved back to the dry sow house.

6. The sow should come into oestrus within 5–7 days.

Management of the sow after weaning

1. The sow is moved to the dry sow house.

2. The sow comes into heat about 5–7 days after weaning.

3. The sow is served by the boar.

4. If the sow fails to come into heat within 10 days, she is given a hormone injection.

> **DOUBLE SERVICING**
> The sow is mated twice within 24 hours. This increases the sows chances of becoming pregnant and it may also increase the litter size.

5. The sow may be culled if she fails to come into heat or fails to become pregnant.

Important minerals and vitamins in the diet of the young pig

The lack of the following minerals and vitamins are all due to the animals being reared indoors.

* Bonhams are prone to suffering from anaemia because the sow's milk is lacking in **iron**. In an outdoor system, this is not a problem because they get sufficient iron from rooting in the soil. Bonhams are given an iron injection when they are 2–3 days old.

* Bonhams may suffer from poor bone formation due to a lack of **vitamin D**.
* Bonhams may also suffer from night blindness due to a lack of **vitamin A**.

These vitamins are added to their feed as food supplements.

Summary

	CALF/COW	LAMB/SHEEP	BONHAM/PIG
Weight at birth	40–45 kg	3–5 kg	1–1.5 kg
Weight at puberty	250 kg	40 kg	75 kg
Weight at slaughter	450–800 kg	30–40 kg	80–82 kg
Gestation period	9½ months	5 months	3 months 3 weeks 3 days
Time to reach slaughter	1–3 years	4–6 months	6 months
Length of oestrous cycle	21 days	17 days	21 days

The aim in animal production is to ensure that all animals reach their full potential. Only healthy animals are able to achieve this.

Disease pressures in animals reared indoors

1. Ideal conditions

* Well-ventilated.

* Draught-free.

* Not overcrowded.

If these conditions are not present, animals may suffer from pneumonia, which can be fatal if not treated. If animals are overcrowded, the disease will spread rapidly, which may result in the death of many animals.

2. Hygiene

This is an important issue when animals are kept indoors because they are in a confined area.

Diseases which may occur as a result of poor hygiene are:

* Navel ill.

* Bacterial scour.

* Clinical mastitis.

(*See* 'Bacterial diseases', page 29.)

3. Diet

Troughs should be cleaned out regularly to prevent a build up of stale food, which may cause illness in animals. Also, bird droppings in feeding troughs can cause scour. Fresh water should also be available. If sufficient feeding area isn't available, some animals may suffer from malnutrition or deficiency diseases.

Fig. 2.1 A trough with fresh water.

Disease pressures in animals reared outdoors

1. **Parasitic diseases:** The eggs of parasitic diseases are usually passed out in the faeces of infected animals. Other animals then ingest these eggs while grazing, resulting in the spread of the disease.

    Examples: Lungworms, stomach worms, intestinal worms, liver flukes.

    The liver fluke is spread by cows/sheep ingesting the encysted cercarium (see page 77). These diseases can be reduced by using the leader–follower system of grazing and by administering a correct dosing regime.

2. **Temperature:** If young animals do not receive an adequate amount of colostrum, it may result in a drop in their body temperature.

    This is more common in lambs because they are more commonly born outdoors – the lambs may become chilled lambs. Chilled lambs should be brought indoors and placed underneath an infrared lamp, they may also need to get a sterile glucose injection.

How to reduce the incidence of disease in animals while outdoors

*   Ensure walkways are kept maintained.
*   Ensure animals have shelter from extreme weather (wind, rain, storm and sun).
*   Keep fields free from dangerous objects.
*   Remove poisonous plants from fields, e.g. ragwort, buttercup.
*   Ensure chemicals are applied at the correct rating and stored properly.

*   If insufficient grazing is available, supplement with concentrates.
*   Prevent mixing with diseased animals.
*   Avoid grazing in infected areas.

Fig. 2.2 Ragwort (above) and buttercup (below).

Outline the disadvantages of overcrowding housed animals

❖ Animals don't have enough air space.

❖ They also don't have enough feeding space.

❖ Sick animals may go unnoticed.

❖ Diseases spread faster.

❖ There is a build-up of manure.

❖ There is insufficient lying space.

❖ All this causes undue stress on animals.

Advantages of the leader–follower system of grazing

✓ Calves and weanlings are first into each paddock.

✓ Yearlings follow and then older animals.

✓ Calves are allowed to graze selectively on young grass, therefore they have a greater LWG.

✓ Older animals are less selective and graze down the remaining grass.

✓ It is a better use of grass.

✓ The level of parasitic worm infestation is reduced.

LWG
Live Weight Gain.

Notifiable diseases

Notifiable diseases (*see* table below) are highly contagious and are a serious national health risk. Suspect animals should be isolated from the rest of the animals and the local vet should be notified. Animals need to be tested to determine whether they have the disease. The confirmed cases are slaughtered.

Isolate.
Notify.
Test.
Slaughter.

CATTLE	SHEEP	PIGS	POULTRY
• Foot and mouth.	• Foot and mouth.	• Foot and mouth.	• Newcastle disease.
• Anthrax.	• Anthrax.	• Anthrax.	
• Rabies.	• Rabies.	• Rabies.	
• BSE.	• Sheep scab.	• Swine fever.	
• TB.	• Scrapie.	• Aujeszki's disease.	
• Brucellosis.			

How to keep animals healthy and prevent the spread of disease

* Ensure newborn animals receive an adequate amount of colostrum.
* Employ a rotational grazing system, preferably the leader–follower system.
* Supervise animals properly.
* Vaccinate and dose animals regularly.
* Have proper housing conditions.
* Treat soils with trace elements to prevent deficiency diseases.
* Remove poisonous weeds from grazing areas.
* Feed animals mineral and vitamin supplements.
* Use veterinary treatment.
* Ensure the animals eat a proper diet.
* Isolate diseased animals.
* Isolate bought-in animals.
* Disinfect equipment used.
* Avoid contact with neighbouring herds.
* Avoid contact with wildlife.

Vaccination of farm animals

Vaccination is giving a non-disease-causing dose of a particular disease. The animals are not infected by the disease at the time of vaccination. The vaccination triggers the immune system to produce antibodies which will help fight the disease in the future. Some vaccines may need to be boosted over time.

Fig. 2.3 A crush: Used when dosing and vaccinating cattle.

DEFICIENCY DISEASES

Anaemia	• Deficiency of iron in the blood. • Occurs in bonhams that are reared indoors. • Animals are listless and fail to thrive (see below). • Give them an iron injection when they are 2–3 days old. • Can occur in calves if they have a heavy infestation of lice. • Treat for lice.
Swayback	• Deficiency of copper. • Occurs in sheep if the grass is deficient in copper. • Animals are unable to stand or walk properly. • Ensure animals have a balanced diet.
Pining	• Deficiency of cobalt. • Occurs in sheep. • Symptoms are poor appetite and poor LWG. • Ensure animals have a balanced diet.
Milk fever	• Deficiency of calcium in the blood. • Occurs in cows after calving. • Animals appear nervous and excitable. • They may be unable to stand up. • Animals enter a coma and death will occur quickly if not treated. • Prevent by giving the cow Cal – Mag.
Lambing sickness	• Same as milk fever. • Occurs in ewes after lambing.
Grass tetany	• Deficiency of magnesium. • Heavily fertilised spring grass has low levels of magnesium. • Animals are unable to store magnesium in the blood. • Animals appear nervous and they have muscles tremors. • Animals enter a coma and death will occur quickly if not treated. • Prevent by giving the animal Cal – Mag.

PARASITIC DISEASES	
Red water fever	• Caused by the parasite Babesia, from the kingdom Protista. • Spread by the common tick. • First identified by the passing of red-coloured urine. • Animals become listless and have a loss of appetite. • Fever and death may follow if not treated. • Prevent by removing the natural environment of the tick (areas of long grass).
Lice	• Animals fail to thrive due to the irritation caused. • Heavy infestation may cause anaemia, especially in calves. • Treat using an insecticide.
Stomach and intestinal worms	• Caused by nematodes. • Most serious in calves. • Animals fail to thrive and have diarrhoea. • Prevent by using the leader–follower system. • Treat by dosing with a suitable nematicide.
Lungworms (hoose, husk)	• Caused by nematodes. • Most serious in calves. • Animals have a hoarse, husky cough and fail to thrive. • May develop into hoose pneumonia if not treated. • Prevent by using the leader–follower system. • Treat by dosing with a suitable nematicide.
Maggots	• Bluebottle and greenbottle flies lay their eggs in the fleece of the sheep. • Eggs hatch and the maggots feed on the flesh of the sheep. • Loss of appetite and listlessness are the first symptoms. • Prevent by dipping sheep.
Sheep scab	• A notifiable disease. • Caused by the mange mite piercing the sheep's skin. • Pustules are produced and form scabs. • Animals appear nervous and their wool falls off. • All sheep must de dipped at least once a year between September 15th and January 31st.

Liverfluke	• Caused by animals ingesting the encysted cercarium.
	• Lives in the bile duct of the sheep/cattle.
	• Failure to thrive, loss of appetite and listlessness.
	• Preventing the spread of liverfluke:
	  1. Drain wetland, therefore the watersnail is not present.
	  2. Put ducks and geese on the land to eat the watersnail.
	  3. Elevate all drinking troughs.
	  4. Fence off wet areas of land.
	  5. Spray the land with a molluscicide to kill the watersnail.
	  6. Apply lime to the land.

BACTERIAL DISEASES	
Navel/joint ill	• Caused by bacteria entering the unhealed navel after the umbilical cord is cut. • The first symptom is a swollen and painful navel. • This can lead to blood poisoning and sudden death. • Prevention: Disinfect the navel with iodine and tie with iodine soaked string at birth.
Bacterial scour	• Caused by unhygienic housing conditions and feeding calves from dirty buckets. • Bacteria build-up in the stomach upsets the digestive system. • Diarrhoea is the first symptom followed by listlessness. • Dehydration and death may follow if not treated. • Treat with antibiotics and feed glucose and water.
Tuberculosis	• A notifiable disease and is also a zoonose. • Symptoms are that the animals fail to thrive and have an unhealthy appearance. **ZOONOSE** A disease that can be transmitted to humans.
Coliform scour	• Caused by E. coli bacteria, due to poor management and hygiene. • Most common in bonhams and weaners up to 8 weeks old. • Diarrhoea and dehydration are the first symptoms. • Death may follow in severe cases. • Treat with antibiotics and feed glucose and water.

Farrowing fever	<ul><li>Infection of the uterus and mammary glands leading to fever and lack of milk.</li><li>Prevent by maintaining good hygiene in the farrowing house.</li><li>Treat with antibiotics.</li></ul>
Brucellosis	<ul><li>A notifiable disease and is also a zoonose.</li><li>Pregnant cows abort their calves during the 5th and 7th months of pregnancy.</li></ul>
Mastitis	<ul><li>Affects the udder of the animal.</li><li>Bacterial (sub-clinical) mastitis: Detected by carrying out the somatic cell count test.</li><li>Clinical mastitis: Swelling and pain in the udder, clots in the milk and general ill health.</li><li>Prevent by maintaining good hygiene on the farm.</li><li>Treat by injecting antibiotics into the teat canal.</li></ul>
Blackleg	<ul><li>Caused by clostridium bacteria.</li><li>These bacteria are found in the soils in certain regions of the country.</li><li>Animals appear lame and have swollen legs.</li><li>Animals become listless and have a high fever.</li><li>The disease spreads rapidly and is nearly always fatal.</li><li>Prevent by injecting animals with an 8 in 1 vaccine.</li></ul>
Footrot	<ul><li>Causes lameness in sheep.</li><li>Affects the animals food intake.</li><li>Treat by removing the infected tissue and spray with an antibiotic.</li><li>Prevent by using a footbath of copper sulphate.</li></ul>

VIRAL DISEASES
Viral pneumonia

Viral pneumonia	<ul><li>Highly infectious disease caused by poor ventilation.</li><li>Coughing is the first symptom and may lead to fever and sudden death if not treated.</li><li>Treat with antibiotics to prevent secondary infection by bacteria.</li><li>Can affect all animals when housed.</li></ul>

SMEDI	• Viral disease in sows. • Stillbirth (S), mummification (M) of embryos, embryonic death (ED) and infertility (I). • Prevent by routine vaccination of sows. • There is no treatment.
Orf (scabby mouth)	• Is a zoonose. • Occurs in sheep. • Pustules and scabs are found on the mouth. • The udder and feet may also be affected. • Is highly infectious. • Ewes are vaccinated 4–6 weeks before lambing. • Lambs are vaccinated at 4 weeks old.

DISEASES CAUSED BY POOR MANAGEMENT	
Lead poisoning	• Caused by calves ingesting lead from paint, used engine oil etc. • This disease is identified by the animals staggering and frothing at the mouth. • Almost always fatal, there is no effective treatment.
Nutritional scour	• Caused by overfeeding or feeding calves at irregular intervals. • A milk ball forms in their stomach causing scour. • Diarrhoea is the first symptom followed by listlessness. • Dehydration and death may follow if not treated. • Feed the calf glucose and water, and then gradually wean back onto milk.
Lameness	• Caused by concrete yards, overcrowding and bad quality slats. • Occurs in cows when housed. • Animals will be lame in one or more legs. • Treat with antibiotics.
Agalactia	• When ewes fail to produce milk after giving birth. • Occurs if mastitis is left untreated from the previous lactation.

Pregnancy toxaemia	• Also known as twin lamb disease. • Occurs if pregnant ewes receive an inadequate amount of nutrition. • Animals become listless and stagger. • Leads to liver malfunction and may result in death if not treated.
Acidosis	• An abnormal increase in the acidity of body fluids. • Occurs if animals are fed too much concentrates or too many root crops too quickly. • Coma and sudden death may occur if animals are not introduced gradually to concentrates and root crops.

OTHER DISEASES	
Bloat	• Caused by animals grazing early grass or high clover swards. • Large quantities of gas is produced, but not released. • The rumen becomes inflated and puts pressure on the heart and lungs. • The animal may die due to suffocation or heart failure. • Treat using a trocar and cannula to release the gases.
Ringworm	• Fungal infection of the skin and hair. • Causes hair loss, itching and failure to thrive. • It is a zoonose disease.

Fig. 2.4 A calf infected with ringworm (notice the white marks on its neck).

3 Soil science

Soil is formed from the underlying rock through an ageing and weathering process.

The ideal soil composition

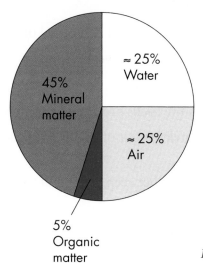

50 per cent soil solids.

50 per cent soil pores.

Fig. 3.1 The ideal soil composition.

The parent material

There are three types of parent material.

* **Residual:** Parent material weathers in situ.
* **Transported:** Parent material is transported and then weathers.
* **Cumulose:** Parent material is derived from decomposing vegetation resulting in the formation of peat soils.

THERE ARE TWO TYPES OF PEAT SOILS

Blanket peat

- Formed in areas with high rainfall and humidity, and low levels of evaporation, which leads to waterlogged conditions.
- Soils are wet, acidic and infertile.
- Blanket peat may form over podzol soils.

Basin peat

- Formed in the basin of a lake or slow moving river.
- They are drier and of more agricultural use.

Factors leading to soil formation

A number of factors influence soil formation and development. Soil is a combination of weathered rock and organic matter.

1. Climate

Climate is the most important factor leading to soil formation.

* The rate of weathering depends on climate.

* Glaciation determines whether the parent material is residual or transported.

* Rocks are broken down by physical and chemical weathering.

    – **Physical:**   Freeze/thaw action shatters rocks.

    – **Chemical:**   ➤ Acid rain reacts with the rocks breaking them down.

    ➤ Rainwater leaches nutrients out of the rocks weakening their structure.

    ➤ **Hydrolysis:** The reaction between water and the parent material.

* Type of vegetation, which influences the soil pH, depends on climate.

2. Parent material

The parent material influences the characteristics of the soil.

* The parent material determines the texture of the soil.

* The mineral composition of rocks varies and influences the mineral content of the soil. Minerals present in the rock will be present in the soil.

* The pH of the rock will determine the pH of the soil.

3. Living organisms

* The organic parent material, e.g. blanket and basin peats, affects soil formation.

* Living organisms contribute nutrients:

    – From their excretory products.

    – When they die (humus).

* Acidity of soil depends on the vegetation.

* Roots of plants cause physical weathering.

* Lichens: These live on bare rock and get their mineral nutrients by secreting

organic acids into the rocks and dissolving the minerals out of it. When they die, they decay and form the first layer of humus.

* All earthworm activities contribute to soil formation (*see* page 40).

4. Topography

Topography affects the depth and type of soil.

* Shallow and less fertile soil on hillsides.

* Deep and fertile soils lower down.

* Water is retained in valley areas and this may lead to peat formation.

* Vegetation is affected by aspect, therefore this may influence pH.

* Frost action is related to altitude.

5. Time

Soils can be formed in 200 years under ideal conditions. It usually takes much longer.

* Irish soils have been formed from glacial drift; therefore, they have been formed after the ice age.

* Soils in Ireland are considered 'young' soils because they were formed over the last 15,000 years.

Physical properties of soil

1. Soil texture

The amount of sand, silt and clay in a soil.

* Most important soil property.

* Influences all other soil properties.

* Almost impossible to change.

SANDY SOIL	CLAY SOIL
• Poor water holding capacity.	• Good water holding capacity.
• Good drainage.	• Poor drainage.
• Good aeration.	• Poor aeration.
• Warms up quickly in the spring.	• Warms up slowly in the spring.
• Not as fertile.	• Fertile soils.
• Easy to cultivate.	• More difficult to cultivate.
• Doesn't retain moisture.	• Retains moisture.

Loam soil possesses a combination of sandy soil and clay soil properties.

2. Soil water

Water is held in the soil by adsorption and capillary forces.

There are three types of water in a soil

1. **Hygroscopic:** Adsorbed water held tightly in the soil – this is not available to plants.

2. **Capillary:** Water held in the spaces between the soil particles – some is available to plants.

3. **Gravitational:** Water found in the large pores – present for short periods after heavy rainfall.

Describing the water content of a soil

* **Saturated:** All pores are filled with water.

* **Field capacity:** Only the capillary pores are filled and the large pores contain air.

* **Permanent wilting point:** Only hygroscopic water is present.

> **AVAILABLE WATER CAPACITY**
> The water extracted by crops between field capacity and permanent wilting point.

The effects of too much water in a soil

* Excess water reduces the amount of soil air.

* Root growth is reduced, therefore reducing the yield of the crop.

* Wet soils warm up slowly, therefore reducing crop growth.

* Wet soils are easily poached and damaged by machinery (*see* definition of 'poaching' at the bottom of this page).

* Wet soils increase the incidence of liver fluke in cattle and sheep.

3. Soil structure

Soil structure is the coming together of the primary soil particles into larger separable units. These separable units are known as aggregates or peds. A soil with a good soil structure has 50 per cent soil solids and 50 per cent soil pores.

Good soil structure is important for the following reasons

* Ensures there is adequate drainage and aeration.

* Allows good root development.

* Makes the soil easy to cultivate.

* Encourages a high population of soil organisms.

Some farm activities that improve soil structure

* Autumn ploughing.

* Removing animals from fields in winter to prevent poaching.

* Applying lime to the soil.

* Carrying out soil cultivations.

* Employing crop rotation.

* Adding organic matter.

* Encouraging the activities of earthworms and other soil organisms.

* Sowing grass – the fibrous roots improve the structure of the soil.

POACHING
Animals compact the soil and damage the soil structure.

PUDDLING
Similar to poaching but animals turn the soil into mud.

Fig. 3.2 Poaching (left) and puddling (right).

STRUCTURE DEVELOPMENT IS A RESULT OF TWO PROCESSES	
Cementation	• Soil particles and cements are pushed closer together.
Separation	• Cemented materials are broken up.
FACTORS RESULTING IN STRUCTURE DEVELOPMENT	
1. Wetting and drying	• Drying causes shrinkage, pushing particles together. Cracks open up in clay soils as it shrinks. This breaks up the soil mass.
2. Freezing and thawing	• Freezing shatters soil clods. • Frost tilth is formed.
3. Activity of roots	• Small roots increase soil and cement contact. • Large roots crack and break up the soil. • When roots die, they increase the pore space.
4. Activity of earthworms and other soil organisms	• Particles and minerals are mixed in the gut. • Channels left by soil organisms break up soils.
5. Tillage operations	• Breaks up the soil. • Exposes the soil to frost action. • Exposes the soil to drying and shrinkage.

4. Soil air

The amount of air in the soil under ideal conditions is 25 per cent. If soil air falls below 8–10 per cent, the crops will fail. Soils with poor aeration also have poor drainage.

Soil organisms require oxygen to survive. Roots need to respire, therefore they also require oxygen. Oxygen and carbon dioxide need to be able to diffuse to and from the root. High levels of carbon dioxide in the soil are toxic to plants.

5. Soil temperature

Every 10 °C rise in soil temperature doubles the rate of crop growth.

Soils with good drainage and aeration will be warmer soils.

Various factors influence soil temperature

* **Water content:** Soils with a high water content warm up slowly.

* **Altitude:** Temperature decreases with altitude.

* **Aspect:** South-facing slopes are warmer than north-facing slopes.

* **Colour:** Soils dark in colour absorb more heat than light-coloured soils.

Chemical properties of soil

1. **Cation exchange capacity:** The ability of soil particles to attract ions onto their surface, hold them there by chemical attraction, and exchange them for others.

   * Cation exchange capacity is a measure of how fertile a soil is.

   * Clay particles and humus have negative charges on their surface and can hold on to cations.

   * The more clay and humus in a soil, the more fertile it is.

2. **Soil pH:** The measurement of the hydrogen ion concentration in a soil.

   * Soils with a low pH have a low number of soil organisms.

   * Low pH affects the breakdown of organic matter.

   * Minerals become unavailable for plant uptake in soils of low pH.

Factors which influence the pH of a soil

* The pH value of the parent material.

* The amount of rainfall.

* Pollution may alter the pH of a soil.

* Fertilizers containing ammonium or urea tend to make soils more acidic.

* The addition of organic matter makes soils more acidic.

> **Granite and sandstone** lead to the formation of acidic soils.
> **Basalt and limestone** lead to the formation of alkaline soils.

Biological properties of soil

1. Soil organisms

Organisms found in the soil include earthworms, centipedes, bacteria, snails and fungi.

Bacteria and fungi play an important role in the decomposition of dead material. Earthworms are the most important soil organism.

* They improve the drainage in a soil.
* They improve the soil aeration.
* They add nutrients from their excretory products.
* They add humus when they die and decay.
* They bring leaves down from the surface.
* They increase the availability of phosphorus by 100 per cent.
* They mix the soil layers.

THE IDEAL SOIL CONDITIONS FOR EARTHWORMS
- pH of between 6 and 8 (ideally between 6.5 and 6.8).
- Moist, but not waterlogged soil conditions.
- A soil temperature of greater than 10 $^{\circ}$C.
- Organic matter present.

---

2. Soil organic matter

This includes humus.

* Humus absorbs water and greatly improves the soil's water holding capacity.
* Humus also contains minerals which are slowly released.

BIOMASS OR HUMUS?

Soil biomass
The total amount of living matter (animal and plant) in a soil.

Soil humus
The remains of dead plants and animals.

Soil profiles

A soil profile is a vertical section of a soil through all its horizons and extending into the parent material.

* **O horizon:** Degraded and non-degraded organic matter.

* **A horizon:** Referred to as topsoil.

* **B horizon:** Referred to as subsoil.

* **C horizon:** The parent material.

Different soil types have different soil profiles:

1. Podzols

The A2 horizon is bleached in colour due to acid leaching.

An iron pan forms in the B2 horizon which is impervious.

The A2 horizon becomes waterlogged.

Blanket peat forms in the O horizon.

* These soils have high lime and fertiliser requirements.

* They may be used for forestry.

* They can be deep ploughed.

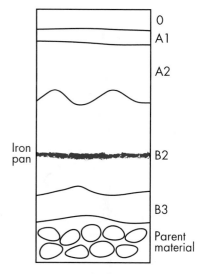

Fig. 3.3 Podzol soil.

How podzolic soils are improved

* The soils may be deep ploughed to break up the iron pan. This will improve the drainage and aeration of a soil.

* Liming the soil will reduce the acidity of the soil.

* Fertilisers will replace the nutrients lost by acid leaching.

2. Grey brown podzol

Grey brown podzol is formed on limestone, therefore no acid leaching.

Clay particles are leached from the A2 horizon.

The clay particles accumulate in the B2 horizon.

* These soils are excellent agricultural soils.

* The clay-rich B2 horizon holds onto moisture during dry summers.

* Good for growing barley.

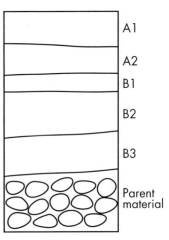

Fig. 3.4 Grey brown podzol.

3. Brown earths

There is an absence of horizons with brown earth soils.

Brown earth soils are among the best soils in Ireland.

Brown earth soils have low lime and fertiliser requirements.

Leaching does occur but not to any great extent.

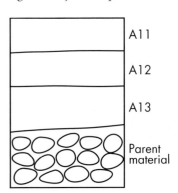

Fig. 3.5 Brown earth.

These characteristics apply only when the brown earths are formed from limestone. If they are formed from an acidic parent material, they are very poor soils.

Liming

Liming has to be carried out due to acid leaching.

It has to be carried out every 5–10 years depending on the soil texture and rainfall.

The advantages of liming

✓ Makes the soil more neutral by removing the acidity.

✓ Crops and grasses respond better to manure.

✓ Improves drainage and aeration by promoting flocculation.

✓ Results in the soil having a better crumb structure.

✓ Adds nutrients and makes nutrients more available.

✓ Increases earthworm activity.

✓ Increases bacterial activity.

✓ Encourages the growth of clover.

✓ Improves the uptake of nutrients.

✓ Reduces the occurrence of liver fluke in cattle and sheep.

✓ The calcium encourages good bone formation in animals.

The disadvantages of liming

❖ The element molybdenum becomes more available, which reduces copper uptake by plants.

❖ Trace elements may become unavailable which could cause deficiency diseases in animals.

❖ Over-liming can damage the structure of light, sandy soils.

The quality requirements of ground limestone

✱ Product must have a TNV of greater than 90 per cent.

✱ The entire product must pass through a 3.35 mm sieve.

> **TNV**
> Total Neutralising Value.

✱ More than 35 per cent of the product must pass through a 0.15 mm sieve.

✱ The moisture content must not exceed 3.0 per cent.

The benefits of adding slurry to soil

✓ Supplies nutrients.

✓ Increases the organic matter content of the soil.

✓ Helps to improve and maintain the soil structure.

✓ Disposes of animal waste.

✓ Encourages better growth of crops.

✓ Improves water retention in soil.

✓ Slurry seeding can be carried out (*see* page 58).

Fig. 3.6 Slurry is applied to the land using a slurry spreader.

4 Grassland

THE THREE TYPES OF GRASSLAND	
1. Rough grazing	• Extremely variable in botanical composition. • Can only support low stocking rates. • Has low levels of production.
2. Permanent grassland	• Dominated by perennial grasses. • Scrub and trees are scarce or absent. • Has never been ploughed.
3. Temporary ley	• Dominated by perennial or Italian ryegrass, and clover. • Can support high stocking rates. • Has very high levels of production.

THE DIFFERENCES BETWEEN A TEMPORARY LEY AND PERMANENT GRASSLAND	
TEMPORARY LEY	**PERMANENT GRASSLAND**
• Reseeded regularly. • More aggressive grass varieties. • Fewer weeds. • Receives more fertiliser. • Low botanical composition. • High productivity. • Can have a high stocking rate.	• Never been ploughed. • Less aggressive grass varieties. • More weeds. • Receives less fertiliser. • Greater botanical composition. • Lower productivity. • Lower stocking rate.

Factors that influence the rate of grass growth

* **Soil type:** This influences soil drainage and aeration.
* **Soil depth:** Deeper soils allow roots more access to water and nutrients.
* **Soil fertility:** There is more growth on fertile soils.
* **Water holding capacity of soil:** Drought and waterlogged soils inhibit grass growth.
* **System of grazing:** Use a rotational grazing system.
* **Weed control:** Weeds reduce grass growth by competing with them.
* **Soil pH:** Ideal pH for grass growth is 6–6.5.
* **Variety of grass sown:** Grasses respond differently to different conditions.

Factors considered when choosing grass varieties to sow

The main factors are:

* Palatability.
* Digestibility.
* Productivity.

Other factors are:

* Aggressiveness of the grass.
* Persistence of the grass.
* Soil type.
* Heading date.

Factors considered when choosing seed mixtures to sow

For grazing

Grazing seed mixtures contain a number of variable strains of perennial ryegrass with a range of heading dates, together with white clover.

* Encourages a uniform growth pattern over the grazing season.

* Increases the feeding value of grass.

* Makes grazing management easier.

For silage

Mixtures for silage are either made up of strains of ryegrass with similar heading dates or contain a single strain only.

Why perennial ryegrass is sown

* Perennial ryegrass is a leafy grass.

* Perennial ryegrass has a long growing season.

* Perennial ryegrass is superior to any other grass in relation to productivity, palatability and digestibility.

* If fertilised adequately, perennial ryegrass can be cut up to four times a year for silage.

* Perennial ryegrass is an aggressive grass and tillers vigorously.

The plant species found in an old pasture

The grass species:

* Cocksfoot.

* Meadow foxtail.

* Yorkshire fog.

Perennial ryegrass would not be present because it requires a soil with good drainage, high fertility and a high pH.

The other species found would be:

* Dock leaves.

* Dandelions.

* Nettles.

* Buttercups.

* Daisies.

* Ragwort.

How to improve this old pasture

* Drain the area if it is waterlogged.

* Carry out a soil test and fertilise accordingly.

* Lime the land to increase the pH and improve drainage.

* Sow superior grass varieties, e.g. perennial ryegrass or Italian ryegrass.

* Sow white clover due to its ability to fix nitrogen.

How the DMD (Dry Matter Digestibility) of grass alters as it matures

DMD is the amount of food/grass that is retained and used by the animal's body.

1. At the leafy stage, grass has a high DMD because most of the carbohydrates are in the form of sugar.

2. As the grass grows taller, the sugar is converted to cellulose (fibre) to support the plant. Cellulose has a much lower DMD than sugar.

3. Once the heading date is reached, most of the sugar has been converted to cellulose.

4. Over time the soluble carbohydrates (sugars) are converted to insoluble carbohydrates (fibre). This results in a decrease in the feeding value of the grass.

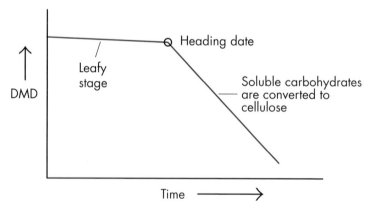

Fig. 4.1 How the DMD of grass alters with time.

The effects of understocking on grass growth

* Results in grass being left uneaten and wasted.

* There is more stemmy growth and therefore lower feeding value.

Solution

* Apply a correct stocking rate.

* Increase the stocking rate in summer when grass growth is high.

> The **ideal height** to graze grass to is 6–7 cm.

The effects of overstocking on grass growth

* Overstocking leads to overgrazing and therefore little growth overall.

* Overstocking weakens the presence of desirable species and therefore decreases production.

* Overstocking encourages the growth of weeds because grasses are less aggressive.

Solution

* Apply a correct stocking rate.

* Reduce the stocking rate or rotate the animals more frequently.

OUTLINE OF THE VARIOUS GRAZING SYSTEMS	
1. SET STOCKING	• A large area is given to the animals at the beginning of the grazing season. • The animals stay there until they are housed again in the autumn. • Worst form of grassland management.
2. BUFFER SYSTEM	• Similar to set stocking, except that an area of grazing is sectioned off using a temporary electric fence. • If grass becomes scarce, the animals are allowed to graze the 'buffer' area. • If grass is plentiful the area may be cut for silage.

3. PADDOCK GRAZING	• Grazing area is divided into 20–25 paddocks. • Paddocks are given a recovery time of about three weeks.
4. STRIP GRAZING	• Similar to paddock grazing, except that an electric fence is used to allocate an area. • Again grass is given about three weeks to recover.
5. LEADER–FOLLOWER SYSTEM	• Calves are allowed to graze one paddock ahead of older cattle. • This system is a method of disease control in young animals. • Young animals also have a greater LWG.
6. CREEP GRAZING	• Used in suckler beef and sheep production. • Where calves/lambs are allowed to graze one paddock ahead of older animals. • Young animals gain access to the paddock ahead by going through a creep gate. • The calves/lambs are able to return to their mothers for suckling.
7. ZERO GRAZING	• Animals don't graze the pastures at all. • Fresh grass is cut on a daily basis and fed to the animals indoors.
8. MIXED GRAZING	• Cattle and sheep graze together.

Advantages of a rotational grazing system

✓ Allows areas to have an adequate recovery time.

✓ Grass is grazed at its most nutritious stage (leafy stage).

✓ Increased productivity.

✓ Better control of diseases, especially if using the leader–follower grazing system.

✓ Better use of grass.

✓ Grasses remain aggressive, therefore reducing the number of weeds.

Factors that influence the length of the grass growing season

* Soil temperature.
* Light intensity.
* Amount of rainfall.
* Soil texture.
* Geographical location.
* Soil air.
* Grass variety.
* Altitude.
* Aspect.

> The **grass growing season** is the length of time that the soil temperature is above 5–6 °C.

Advantages of a mixed grazing system

✓ Better use of grass because sheep eat the grass around dung pats, whereas cattle will not.
✓ The way in which sheep graze increases tillering because they graze closer to the ground.
✓ Due to the increased tillering, there is a higher yield of grass produced.
✓ Helps with weed control because grasses are more competitive.
✓ Easier to manage all stock.
✓ Greater recycling of nutrients due to the composition of cattle and sheep dung and urine.
✓ Cattle have a greater LWG because they are allowed to graze selectively.

Fertiliser requirements of grass to be harvested as silage

The area is fertilised at least six weeks before cutting.

1. 100–200 kilograms per hectare (kg/ha) of nitrogen (N) is applied for the first cut.
2. 80–100 kg/ha of N is applied for the second cut.
3. 60–80 kg/ha of N is applied for the third cut.

If too much nitrogen fertiliser is applied or applied too late, it may reduce the silage quality. The amount of phosphorus (P) and potassium (K) depends on how much slurry was applied to the land. High fertility is required to maintain perennial ryegrass and to keep the area weed free.

The two methods of conserving grass

Controlled fermentation (i.e. silage) or dehydration (i.e. hay).

1. **Controlled fermentation** reduces the pH of the grass to a level at which all bacterial activity stops.

2. **Dehydration** reduces the moisture content of the grass to a level of dryness at which all bacterial activity stops.

Practices involved in producing good-quality silage

1. Close off field.

2. Add the correct amount of fertiliser.

3. Allow six weeks growing time.

4. Cut the grass at the correct stage, when the DMD is high.

5. Cut as early as possible, first cut should be harvested around the 20th May.

6. Cut in dry weather.

7. Harvest the grass using a double chop or precision chop harvester.

8. Allow the grass to wilt.

9. Bale or transport the grass to the pit at this stage.

10. Fill the pit quickly.

11. Shake out the grass to prevent the formation of air pockets.

12. Apply an additive if required.

13. Pack the pit properly.

> **FYM**
> Farm Yard Manure.

14. Cover the pit with two layers of heavy gauge polyethene plastic.

15. Weigh down the plastic with tyres or FYM.

Fig. 4.2 A silage pit.

Practices involved in producing good-quality hay

1. Cut when the weather is dry.

2. Aim to have all the hay saved by the end of June.

3. Cut when the grass is at the correct stage of growth.

4. Cut the grass using a rotary mower.

5. Cut in manageable amounts.

6. Shake up the grass immediately after cutting.

7. Turn the grass frequently to ensure fast drying.

8. Put the grass into rows.

9. Bale when moisture is down to 25 per cent.

10. Bring into final storage when it has reached 20 per cent.

Fig. 4.3 A rotary turner.

Advantages of hay over silage

✓ No need for the construction of silage storage areas.

✓ Hay is more suitable if fields are scattered from the main yard.

✓ Rough or wet land is unsuitable for silage making machinery.

Advantages of silage over hay

✓ Silage has a higher DMD.

✓ Silage is not dependent on a long spell of sunshine.

✓ Silage is more palatable.

✓ Silage making is fully mechanised.

✓ Silage can be cut up to three times in one year.

✓ Silage can be cut as early as May.

✓ A self-feeding method can be used to feed silage over the winter.

The advantages of producing silage in round bales

✓ Suitable for small farms.

✓ Easily bought and sold.

✓ Convenient for use.

✓ Less pollution risk.

✓ No need for a pit for storage.

Fig. 4.4 Round bales.

Applying additives to grass being preserved as silage

Additives are applied to ensure lactic acid silage is produced. There are four main types of additives.

TYPES OF ADDITIVES	
1. Stimulants	• Source of carbohydrates. • Carbohydrates ensure the presence of lactobacillus and streptococci bacteria. • Molasses contains 53 per cent sucrose. It is applied to each layer of grass in the pit at a rate of 10 litre per tonne of cut grass.
2. Acids	• Acids rapidly lower the pH in the silage pit. • The low pH encourages lactobacillus activity. • Examples are propanoic and sulphuric acid. • Acids are applied at a rate of 3–5 litre per tonne of cut grass. • Acids are applied during the cutting operations. • Acids are not applied on the last load of the day.
3. Enzymes	• Enzymes are biological catalysts. • Enzymes are applied to speed up the fermentation process.
4. Bacteria	• The pit may be inoculated with lactobacillus and streptococci bacteria. This increases the number of desirable bacteria.

The importance of tillering in the establishment of a good grassland sward

Tillering is required for good grassland establishment.

* Tillering helps develop a close sward with a well-developed **root mat**. The root mat supports grazing animals and prevents poaching.

* Tillering is encouraged by grazing newly sown pastures with light stock, e.g. **calves or sheep**. They encourage tillering by defoliation and damage to the main shoots of the plants. Repeated grazing and topping encourages tillering; this prevents the establishment of weeds.

Weed control in the establishment of a good grassland sward

* Encourage **tillering** by grazing and topping. Weeds compete with grass plants for light, space, nutrients and moisture. If dock leaves are a problem, they can be removed by spraying with a selective herbicide. Other weeds, e.g. ragwort can be removed by hand.

* Apply **slurry** sparingly. Slurry will burn out grass and allow weeds to grow on the bare patches. Also, the high potassium levels found in slurry favours dock growth. Slurry may smother young tillers.

The importance of soil fertility in the establishment of a good grassland sward

The level of soil fertility influences the rate of tillering. Tillering is very important during the period of grassland establishment. First, carry out a soil test and then apply N, P and K accordingly. The fertiliser may be applied at the time of sowing. Lime the soil to control the pH.

The advantages of clover

✓ Clover increases the palatability of the sward.
✓ Clover increases the productivity of the sward over the summer months.
✓ Clover increases the protein content of the sward.
✓ Clover has a high mineral content.
✓ Clover spreads using stolons; this ensures good ground cover and reduces the number of weeds.
✓ And most importantly, clover has the ability to fix nitrogen (*see* page 57).

> **Clover** prefers a pH of between 6.5 and 6.8.
> If the field is heavily fertilised with nitrogen fertiliser, clover becomes redundant and begins to die off.

THE DIFFERENCES BETWEEN WHITE AND RED CLOVER	
WHITE CLOVER	**RED CLOVER**
• Has a white flower.	• Has a red/pink flower.
• A short plant.	• A taller plant.
• Has a creeping growth habit.	• Has an erect growth habit.
• Has no hair on the leaves or stem.	• Has hairs on the leaves and stem.
• Has small leaves.	• Has large leaves.
• Good at fixing nitrogen.	• Not as good at fixing nitrogen.
• Good quality.	• Not as good quality.
• Persistent.	• Not as persistent.

Nitrogen fixation growth

Nitrogen fixation is the conversion of atmospheric nitrogen (N_2) into nitrates (NO_3).

Plants require nitrogen to make protein; plants can only absorb nitrogen in the form of NO_3. Clover has developed a symbiotic relationship with Rhizobium bacteria. These bacteria carry out the nitrogen fixation. The Rhizobium bacteria live in the root nodules of the clover plant. Some of the NO_3 is used by the bacteria and some is absorbed by the clover plant. The excess NO_3 is released into the soil air and is available to the grass plants. This reduces the amount of N fertiliser that needs to be applied to the land.

METHODS OF SOWING GRASS SEEDS	
1. Direct sowing	• Most reliable way to sow a good ley. • A fine seedbed is prepared. • The seeds are sown using a combined drill or broadcast onto the soil and covered using a chain harrow.
2. Undersowing	• Commonly used in tillage/grassland rotations. • The seeds are usually sown with a spring cereal. • The spring cereal is referred to as the nurse crop. • The two crops grow together over the summer. • After the cereal has been harvested, establishment and utilisation of the grassland begins.

3. Direct drilling	<ul><li>Grass seeds are drilled into unploughed ground.</li><li>The grass is killed off using a herbicide.</li><li>Fertiliser and slug pellets are drilled into the soil with the grass seeds.</li><li>Done on shallow, stony or hilly soils.</li><li>Also carried out on soils that are subject to poaching; the root mat gives extra strength.</li></ul>
4. 'Stitching in'	<ul><li>Similar to direct drilling.</li><li>The old grassland is not killed.</li><li>The old grassland is severely grazed and the amount of nitrogen applied is reduced.</li><li>A small amount of a herbicide may also be used.</li><li>The seed, fertiliser and slug pellets are drilled into cultivated slits.</li></ul>
5. Slurry seeding	<ul><li>Most unreliable method. Grass seeds are either mixed with slurry and spread on the pasture or the seed is spread first and the slurry applied after.</li><li>May extend the life of Italian ryegrass over a number of years.</li><li>Only successful if there is bare soil present and adequate rainfall.</li></ul>

5 Crop production

Varieties available

* **Barley:** Winter barley and spring barley.
* **Potatoes:** First earlies, second earlies, main crop.
* **Sugarbeet:** Number of varieties available.

Factors considered when choosing a variety

Barley

These are some of the factors farmers may take into consideration.

* Yield.
* Quality of the grain.
* Standing power.
* Earliness of ripening.
* Weight of the grain.
* Resistance to disease.
* Length of the straw.
* Seed availability.

Potatoes

These are some of the factors farmers may take into consideration.

* Yield.
* Eating quality.
* Keeping quality.
* Resistance to disease.
* Saleability.
* Seed availability.
* Maturity.

Sugarbeet

* The variety is chosen by taking the soil type and location of the farm into consideration.

Place in rotation

* **Barley:** Barley is not seriously affected by soil-borne pests and diseases. There is no set time for rotation.

* **Potatoes:** Sow no more than once every three years.

* **Sugarbeet:** No beet or Brassica crop should be sown more than once every three years.

SOIL SUITABILITY	
Barley	<ul><li>Deep, sandy loam soils.</li><li>Brown earths and grey brown podzolics.</li><li>Good drainage.</li><li>pH 6–6.5.</li></ul> **GREY BROWN PODZOLICS** The clay rich B2 horizon retains moisture during the growing season.
Potatoes	<ul><li>Deep, well-drained, sandy loam soils.</li><li>pH 5.</li><li>Stone-free.</li><li>Light, sandy soils and south facing slopes for first earlies.</li></ul>
Sugarbeet	<ul><li>Deep, well-drained, loam soils.</li><li>pH 6.5–7.</li></ul>

SEEDBED PREPARATION	
Winter barley	<ul><li>Plough and harrow.</li><li>No rolling after sowing; this leads to soil capping.</li></ul> **SOIL CAPPING** The breakdown of structure in the top few millimetres of a soil.
Spring barley	<ul><li>Autumn plough and harrow.</li><li>Roll after sowing.</li></ul>
Potatoes	<ul><li>Autumn plough to a depth of 22 cm.</li><li>A fine seedbed is required.</li><li>Ridges should be high and wide.</li></ul>

| Sugarbeet | • Autumn plough.
• A deep fine seedbed is required. |

	SOWING THE SEEDS
Barley	• Seeds are sown using a combined drill in lines 18 cm apart. • Sowing rate for spring barley is 125–140 kg/ha. • Sowing rate for winter barley is greater than required for spring barley. The higher seeding rate is required because there is a lower percentage establishment in winter barley.
Potatoes	• Seeds are sown 10 cm below the surface of the ridge. • Ridges should be 76 cm apart. • Potatoes may be sprouted prior to planting. • As the size of the seed increases, the number of 'eyes' increases. • Each eye grows into an individual plant. • Seeds are sown using an automatic or semi-automatic planter. • Seeds 35–45 mm in diameter should be spaced 20–25 cm apart. • Seeds 45–55 mm in diameter should be spaced 30–35 cm apart. **SPROUTING POTATOES** The seeds are placed in shallow, sprouting boxes; these boxes are then placed in greenhouses or well-lit buildings at a temperature of 5.5 °C or greater. Sprouting speeds up growth, plant emergence and yield. Sprouting seeds of the main crop can increase yield by up to 5 tonnes/ha. This is essential for first earlies.
Sugarbeet	• Seeds are sown using a precision seeder. • Seeds are spaced 18 cm apart in drills 56 cm apart.

CLIMATE	
Barley	• Steady supply of moisture during growing season. • Dry conditions at ripening and harvesting. • Spring barley is not frost resistant.
Potatoes	• Potatoes are not frost resistant. • Mild showery weather during the growing season. • Drought causes a reduction in yield.
Sugarbeet	• Mild showery weather during the growing season. • Sunshine. The sugar content is influenced by the amount of sunshine during the growing season.

FERTILISER REQUIREMENTS	
Barley	• Use a soil test to determine the amount of **nitrogen, phosphorous** and **potassium** required by the crop.

Potatoes	• Carry out a soil test – the usual rates applied are:
	   – **Nitrogen:** 125–150 kg/ha.
	   – **Phosphorous:** 125–150 kg/ha.
	   – **Potassium:** 250–300 kg/ha.

Sugarbeet	• **Nitrogen, phosphorous and potassium:** Required for normal crop growth.
	   – **Boron:** Prevents heart rot.
	   – **Sodium:** Derived from the salt-loving sea beet.
	   – **Manganese:** Prevents speckled yellows.

WEED CONTROL	
Barley	• Crop rotation. • Stubble cleaning. • Herbicides.

Potatoes	• Residual herbicide. • Shading. • Earthing up.
Sugarbeet	• Contact and residual herbicides.

DISEASE CONTROL	
Barley	• Powder mildew: Fungal disease. • Leaf blotch: Fungal disease. • Loose smut: Fungal disease. For the above diseases, spray the crop with a systemic fungicide. • Barley yellow dwarf virus: Viral disease. This disease is spread by aphids, it is prevented by spraying the crop with an insecticide.
Potatoes	• Blackleg: Bacterial disease. Avoid badly drained fields and storing wet tubers. • Gangrene: Fungal disease. Spray the crop with a systemic fungicide. • Common scab: Occurs if potatoes are sown in soils with a high pH. Do not apply lime to the potato crop or the previous crop. • Potato blight: Fungal disease. Spray with a systemic fungicide. • Leaf roll: Viral disease. • Leaf mosaics: Viral disease. Both leaf roll and leaf mosaics are spread by aphids. They are prevented by spraying the crop with an insecticide.
Sugarbeet	• Virus yellow: Viral disease. This disease is spread by aphids, it is prevented by spraying the crop with an insecticide. • Blackleg: Fungal disease. Spray the crop with a systemic fungicide.

PEST CONTROL	
Barley	• Wireworms: Use certified seed and/or poison baits. • Leatherjackets: Use certified seed and/or poison baits. • Aphids: Use insecticides or ladybirds.

Potatoes	• Wireworms: Use poison baits. • Slugs: Use slug pellets. • Aphides: Use insecticides or ladybirds. • Potato cyst nematode: Employ crop rotation.
Sugarbeet	• Aphids: Use insecticides or ladybirds. • Beet cyst nematode: Employ crop rotation.

HARVESTING	
Barley	• When the crop is ready, it is harvested using a combined harvester.
Potatoes	• Haulms killed off three weeks prior to harvesting. • Use an elevator digger or a complete potato harvester. **HAULMS** The stem and leaves of the potato plant.
Sugarbeet	• Harvested from mid-September using special sugarbeet harvesters.

YIELD	
Barley	• Winter barley: 7–8 tonnes per hectare (tonnes/ha). • Spring barley: ≈ 5 tonnes/ha.
Potatoes	• First earlies: 7–10 tonnes/ha. • Main crop: 30–40 tonnes/ha.
Sugarbeet	• Roots: 40 tonnes/ha. • Tops: 25–30 tonnes/ha.

STORAGE	
Barley	• Drying. • Acid treatment.

Potatoes	• Well-ventilated.
	• Frost and leak proof.
	• Easy access for tractors and trailers.
Sugarbeet	• Concrete yards/very dry firm ground.
	• Clamps: long and narrow, < 2.5 m high.

Barley

The indications that the barley crop is ready for harvesting

* The crop is bleached in colour.

* The grain is dry and hard.

* The ear (seedhead) bends over and lies parallel to the stem.

* The crop has a high DM.

* The flag leaf is withered.

The advantages of sowing winter barley over sowing spring barley

✓ Winter barley has a higher yield.

✓ Winter barley is ready for harvesting earlier.

✓ Bad weather in the spring can seriously delay seedbed preparation and sowing.

✓ On mixed farms, sowing winter barley lowers the workload in spring.

✓ There is less of a demand for machinery in the autumn time.

The ideal date to sow winter barley and why

* October 1st is the ideal date.

* Barley has to reach the grass corn stage before growth stops for the winter.

* Once the grass corn stage has been reached, the crop is frost resistance.

* The grass corn stage is when the crop is 8–10 cm in height.

If sown too early, the crop gets too tall and lodges. If sown too late, it doesn't reach the grass corn stage and is killed off by frost over the winter.

The ideal date to sow spring barley and why

Spring barley is not frost resistant and therefore is sown after the last frosts.

The storage of cereal crops

1. Drying

* Grain is dried to 14 per cent moisture. This prevents the germination or sprouting of grain. It also prevents attacks by bacteria, fungi, insects and pests.

* High moisture content at harvesting increases the cost of drying the grain.

* Drying can result in the cereal being very dusty and can be expensive.

2. Acid treatment

* If the grain is required for rolling or grinding, a higher moisture content is required.

* The grain is sprayed with either propanoic or sulphuric acid at a rate of 3–5 litres per tonne. This prevents sprouting by killing the embryo of the seed. The low pH and acidic taste prevents attacks by bacteria, fungi, insects and pests.

Feeding barley to ruminants verses non-ruminants

1. **Ruminants:** Barley just needs to be rolled; once the husk (seed coat) is broken, it can be digested.

2. **Non-ruminants:** The barley has to be ground into small pieces so that it can be broken down by the digestive enzymes.

Potatoes

Earthing up

Earthing up is when the ridger is driven through the crop. It results in the widening of ridges and the deepening of furrows.

The advantages of earthing up in potatoes

✓ Increases the yield.

✓ Prevents 'greening' of tubers.

✓ Prevents tubers being infected by blight.

✓ Uproots weeds.

✓ Protects tubers from being attacked by pests.

✓ Supports the stem.

How potato blight affects crop growth

Tiny branches of the hyphae, called haustoria, penetrate the cell wall and digest and absorb the organic matter. This results in the leaves first turning brown and then black, this prevents the plant from photosynthesing and affects the yield. If the zoospores infect the tubers, they rot during storage.

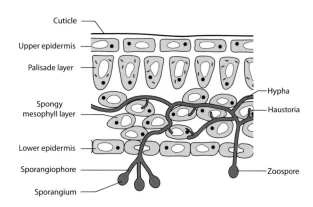

Fig. 5.1 Potato blight.

Conditions that favour the spread of potato blight

1. The zoospores of blight are light and can travel large distances in the wind.

2. The zoospores germinate when the temperature is greater than 20 °C and moisture is present. When these conditions are expected, warnings are issued by the Irish Meteorological Service. At this stage, farmers should spray their potato crop every 10–14 days with a systemic fungicide.

Why the haulms are killed off three weeks prior to harvesting

The haulms are killed off using a contact herbicide.

* It allows the skins of the potatoes to toughen up.

* This reduces the damage to the potatoes at harvesting.

* Damaged potatoes are more susceptible to bacterial infection during storage.

* Removing the haulms also makes harvesting easier.

Sugarbeet

Feeding sugarbeet tops to animals

Sugarbeet tops contain the toxin oxalic acid, which causes scour in animals.

* The tops should be left to wilt for one week to allow the oxalic acid to break down.

* The tops may be fed in situ.

* The tops may be fed using strip grazing.

* The tops may be removed from the field and fed indoors.

* The tops may be ensiled.

Sugarbeet harvesters

1. The sugarbeet roots are lifted from the ground.

2. The tops are cut off and returned to the field.

3. The roots are transferred to a trailer or a storage hopper.

Catch crops

The advantages of catch crops

✓ Catch crops have high yields.

✓ Catch crops can be used as winter feeding for animals.

✓ Catch crops contain highly digestible nutrients.

✓ Catch crops prevent nutrients being leached out of the soil.

✓ Catch crops enable crop rotation to be carried out.

✓ Catch crops use the same cultivation machinery as tillage crops.

✓ Catch crops control weeds by shading.

> **CATCH CROP**
>
> A crop grown between two main crops when the land would otherwise be idle, e.g. rape and kale.

The disadvantages of catch crops

❖ Catch crops increase the workload for the farmer.

❖ Catch crops need to be stored over winter.

How catch crops are fed to farm animals

✳ Catch crops can be grazed in situ.

✳ Catch crops can be harvested and fed outdoors.

✳ Catch crops can be harvested, pulped and fed indoors.

Crop production

List the characteristics of certified seed

✳ Seed has a minimum of 85 per cent germination rate.

✳ Seed has a minimum of 98 per cent analytical purity.

✳ Seed is free from wild oat seeds.

✳ Seed is treated with a systemic fungicide and contact insecticide.

> Certified seed is seed that is produced by the Department of Agriculture and Food under strictly controlled conditions.

Advantages of using certified seed

✓ Seed has a high percentage germination.

✓ Crop has a better rate of establishment.

✓ Seed has a higher yield.

✓ There are fewer weeds.

✓ Seed is true to type.

✓ There are fewer pests and diseases.

✓ It is easier to market the crop.

How crop diseases are prevented and controlled

✳ Monitor the growth of the crop.

✳ Use certified seed.

✳ Sow resistant varieties.

✳ Employ crop rotation.

✳ Carry out autumn ploughing.

* Spray the crop when required.

* Remove diseased plants.

* Harvest the crop once it's ready.

* Encourage growth by using the correct fertilisers.

Viral diseases in crops

Viral diseases attack all crops. There are two main ways in which they are spread – aphids and contact.

* A diseased plant coming in **contact** with another plant will spread the disease. To prevent this, remove diseased plants.

> Ladybirds are predators of aphids. The common name for aphids is greenfly.

* **Aphids** gain their nutrition by removing cell sap from plants. Aphids spread the disease by removing sap from a diseased plant and then infecting subsequent plants. Control aphids chemically by spraying the crop with insecticides or biologically by introducing ladybirds.

Methods of controlling pests, weeds and diseases without using chemicals

* **Crop rotation:** Different conditions from year to year discourage a build up of weeds; and soil-borne pests and diseases associated with a particular crop.

* **Growth encouragement:** Healthy vigorous crops disallow the build up of weeds; also shading occurs quicker.

* **Earthing up:** Uproots weeds and prevents infection of tubers with blight.

* **Sow resistant varieties:** This prevents the crop from suffering from certain diseases.

* **Harvest without delay:** When crops become over ripe, they are more susceptible to damage by pests and diseases.

* **Stubble cleaning:** Harrow the ground to encourage weed seeds to germinate. Harrow the ground again to kill weed seedlings.

* **Autumn ploughing:** Weeds, pests and diseases are exposed to frost over the winter and killed.

* **Biological control:** Ladybirds are natural predators of aphids.

Chemical methods of controlling pests, weeds and diseases

There are different types of chemicals: herbicides, fungicides, insecticides. They can be contact, systemic, total, selective or residual.

* **Contact herbicides:** Only kill or protect what they touch – more coverage required.

* **Systemic herbicides:** Absorbed by the plant – less coverage required.

* **Total herbicides:** Kill all plants.

* **Selective herbicides:** Only kill certain plants.

* **Residual herbicides:** Forms a layer of herbicide under the surface of the soil. They are absorbed by weed seeds as they germinate.

The importance of weed control in crop production

Weeds compete with crops for light, space, nutrients and water.

* Weeds affect the establishment, development and the yield of the crop.

* The presence of weeds also makes harvesting more difficult.

The advantages of crop rotation

✓ **Disease and pest control:** Many soil-borne pests and diseases are specific to a crop or group of crops. The organisms must be starved out by growing crops unsuitable to them.

✓ **Maintaining soil structure and increasing organic matter content:** Organic matter content is improved and increased under grassland. When the grass is ploughed under, subsequent crops benefit from good soil structure and high organic matter content.

✓ **Weed control:** Different cultivations and sowing dates prevent the build up of weeds associated with any individual crop.

The advantages of autumn ploughing

✓ The soil is exposed to the effects of the weather over the winter.
✓ It is easier to cultivate the land in spring.
✓ There is earlier sowing of the crop in springtime, resulting in higher yields.
✓ Soil-borne pests and diseases, and weed seeds are killed over the winter.

Summary

Choice of variety	• Disease resistant varieties. • Use certified seed.
Soil suitability	• Dry conditions at sowing and harvesting are required. • Deep and stone-free soils for root crops are required. • Well-drained.
Sowing the seeds	• Spacing is necessary to ensure the crop is not overcrowded and also that no space is wasted.
Climate	• Dry conditions at sowing and harvesting are required. • Constant supply of moisture is necessary during the growing season.
Fertiliser requirements	• Carry out a soil test.
Weed control	• Utilise crop rotation.
Pest control	• Utilise crop rotation.
Harvesting	• Dry conditions are necessary. • Should be carried out when the crop is ready.

6 Classification of organisms

All living organisms are divided into five kingdoms. Each one of the five kingdoms will be dealt with in detail in this chapter.

The kingdom Animalia is subdivided into phyla and the kingdom Plantae is subdivided into families. You are required to be able to classify members of the kingdom Animalia and Plantae into their respective phylum or family.

Living organisms are divided into five kingdoms

1. Kingdom Monera.
2. Kingdom Animalia.
3. Kingdom Protista.
4. Kingdom Fungi.
5. Kingdom Plantae.

Kingdom Monera

Bacteria

Bacteria are members of the kingdom Monera.

The growth of bacteria depends on the presence of a number of factors:

* Moisture.
* Correct temperature.
* Correct pH.
* Food source.

The advantages of bacteria in agriculture

✓ Lactobacillus and streptococci bacteria produce silage.
✓ Soil bacteria carry out decomposition releasing nutrients.
✓ Rhizobium bacteria fix nitrogen.
✓ Bacteria are involved in the nitrogen cycle.
✓ They digest cellulose in the rumen.
✓ They produce vitamins in the intestine of the animal.

✓ They are required for the production of some dairy products.

✓ They are involved in the production of some antibiotics.

The disadvantages of bacteria in agriculture

❖ They cause numerous diseases in both plants and animals.

❖ They result in the rotting of crops during storage.

❖ Bacteria cause milk to go sour.

Kingdom Animalia

The kingdom Animalia is divided into phyla.

PHYLUM	MEMBERS	CHARACTERISTICS
Annelida	• Earthworms	• The body is segmented internally and externally. • Earthworms are hermaphrodites. • They have a circulatory system. • They have a coelom.
Arthropoda	• Aphids • Ticks • Mites • Leatherjackets • Wireworms, etc.	• Commonly known as the insects. • They have jointed limbs. • They have an exoskeleton. • The body is divided in three: head, thorax and abdomen. • Insects undergo metamorphosis. • Gaseous exchange occurs through spiracles.
Nematoda	• Potato cyst nematodes • Beet cyst nematodes • Lungworms • Stomach worms • Intestinal worms	• Nematodes have a cylindrical body shape. • Their body is covered in a tough cuticle. • They have no circulatory system.
Mollusca	• Slugs • Watersnails	• Molluscs are soft-bodied animals. • They have a foot. • The foot produces slime which helps with movement. • They have a coelom.

Platyhelminthes	• Liverflukes • Tapeworms	• Also known as the flatworms. • They have no coelom. • They are dorso-ventrally flattened. • They have no circulatory system. • The liverfluke is a hermaphrodite.
Chordata	• Cattle • Sheep • Pigs • Poultry	• Chordates are warm-blooded. • They produce milk to feed their young. • They possess a backbone. • They have a well-developed brain and spinal cord.

COELOM

A fluid-filled cavity that functions as a hydroskeleton and also provides space for the development of internal organs.

The pressure of the fluid and action of the surrounding muscles help the animal to move.

Annelida

The earthworm contributes many advantages to the soil (*see* Chapter 3, page 40).

Arthropoda

* Aphids spread viral diseases in plants.

* Ticks, mites and lice are ectoparasites of animals.

* Leatherjackets and wireworms are crop pests.

The benefits of insects in agriculture

✓ Insects carry out pollination.
✓ Ladybirds are predators of aphids (biological control).
✓ Insects, such as the dung beetle, recycle organic matter.

The harmful effects of insects in agriculture

❖ Aphids spread viral diseases in plants.
❖ The tick spreads Babesia in cattle.

METAMORPHOSIS

The change in size and structure of the insect body as it grows and matures.

Incomplete metamorphosis

The young insect resembles the adult in body structure.

These insects undergo many small changes until they become adults.

Egg → Nymph → Adult

Examples: Cockroach, grasshopper.

Complete metamorphosis

The young insect looks nothing like the adult.

These insects undergo one dramatic change and become adults.

Egg → Larva → Pupa → Adult

Examples: Maggots → Bluebottle flies
Caterpillar → Butterfly
Wireworm → Click beetle
Leatherjacket → Crane fly

❖ Ticks, lice and mites are parasites of animals.

❖ Wireworms, leatherjackets, etc. cause damage to crops.

Nematoda

* Animal parasites are known as roundworms.

* Plant parasites are known as eelworms.

* Free-living nematodes can be beneficial by breaking down organic matter.

Mollusca

* Slugs are a pest of most crops. Slugs eat into potatoes exposing them to bacterial infection during storage.

* The watersnail is the secondary host of the liverfluke.

PARASITE

An organism that lives off another organism causing it harm.

Endoparasites

Live inside their host.

Ectoparasites

Live on the outside of their host.

Platyhelminthes

The most important member is the liverfluke.

* The liverfluke has an oral sucker and a ventral sucker which help it attach itself to its host.

* The liverfluke's body wall is coated with a tough cuticle to protect it against the host's defences.

* The liverfluke is an endoparasite of both cattle and sheep.

* The liverfluke lives in the bile duct of the cattle/sheep.

* Mostly a problem on wetland.

The lifecycle of the liverfluke

1. The fertilised eggs are egested via the small and large intestines.

2. If the conditions are suitable, i.e. greater then 10 °C and a pH of less then 7.5, the eggs hatch. The miracidium emerges from the egg – this stage is free-living.

3. The miracidium has 24 hours to find a watersnail.

4. Once the miracidium enters the watersnail its body structure changes. It is now referred to as the sporocyst.

5. Asexual reproduction occurs inside the body of the sporocyst resulting in the next stage known as the redia.

6. Asexual reproduction occurs inside the body of the redia resulting in the next stage known as the cercarium.

7. The cercaria leave the body of the watersnail.

8. The cercaria uses its tail to swim up a blade of grass, there it encysts and waits to be eaten.

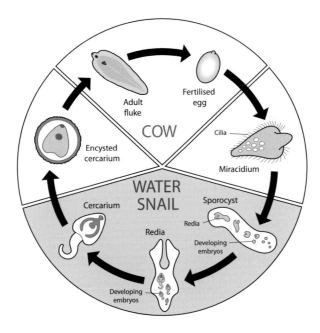

Fig. 6.1 The lifecycle of the liverfluke.

Kingdom Protista

The Kingdom Protista was previously known as the Phylum Protozoa.

Characteristics of the kingdom:

 * Single-celled animals.

 * Reproduces by binary fission.

Important members of the kingdom Protista:

1. *Babesia.*

    − *Babesia* causes redwater fever in cattle.

    − *Babesia* is spread by the common tick.

2. Protozoans in the rumen.

    − Protozoans found in the rumen help in the digestion of cellulose.

Kingdom Fungi

Fungi are found anywhere there is organic matter.

 * Fungi reproduce asexually by budding.

 * Fungi reproduce sexually by producing spores.

The body of a fungus is the mycelium, which is made up of thread-like fibres called hyphae. Fungi obtain their nutrition through extracellular digestion.

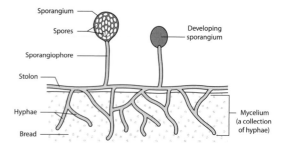

Fig. 6.2 The bread mould, Mucor.

Kingdom Plantae

Flowering plants can be divided in two: 1. Monocots.

2. Dicots.

┌─────────────────────────────┐
| **COTYLEDON** |
| The food store in the seed. |
└─────────────────────────────┘

MONOCOTS	DICOTS
• Monocots have one cotyledon in their seed. • Leaves have parallel venation. • Vascular bundles are scattered in the stem. • Monocots have a fibrous root system. • Examples are grasses, cereals, onion and daffodil.	• Dicots have two cotyledons in their seed. • Leaves have netted venation. • Vascular bundles are arranged in a ring in the stem. • Dicots have a taproot. • Examples are sugar beet, potato, carrot and strawberry.

Monocot and dicot plants can be divided further into families.

Plant families of agricultural interest

Graminea

All grasses and cereals are members of the family graminea.

* All members have the ability to tiller.

* Plants are wind pollinated.

Leguminosae (the legumes)

Examples are clover, peas, beans and gorse.

* All members of this family have the ability to fix nitrogen.

* The flower provides a stage called a keel, for the pollinator.

* Seeds are produced in pods.

* The seeds are self-dispersed.

Compositae

Examples are daisy, dandelion, ragwort and thistle.

* The 'flower' is a collection of many florets.

* Florets are borne together on a flat receptacle.

  * Ragwort is poisonous to livestock.

Cruciferae (the cabbage family)

Examples are rape, kale and cabbage.

  * Flower parts occur mainly in fours.

  * The flower is in the form of a cross.

Rape and kale are grown as catch crops.

Rosacaea (the rose family)

Examples are rose, apple, strawberry, cherry, plum and pear.

  * Flowers are made up of five petals and five sepals, numerous stamens and carpels.

Solanaceae

Examples are potato and tomato. Haulms of the potato plant are poisonous.

Chenopodeaceae

An example is sugar beet. Sugar beet tops contain oxalic acid.

Ranunculus

An example is buttercup. Buttercups are poisonous to animals. If eaten, they result in severe irritation of the mouth and digestive system. The plant is harmless to livestock when made into hay.

Umbelliferae (the carrot family)

Examples are carrot, parsnip, parsley, dill and celery.

  * The inflorescence is typically borne on spikes somewhat like an umbrella.

7 Animal physiology

In this chapter, the systems of the animal's body and their functions are explained.

For animals to achieve their full potential, i.e. produce the maximum amount of milk, give birth to healthy offspring, produce good quality meat, etc., all their systems need to be functioning properly.

The animal's body is made up of **cells**.

* A **tissue** is a group of cells which perform the same function.
* An **organ** is a structure containing a group of tissues with a similar function.
* A **system** is a number of organs working together to carry out a function.

The digestive system

Animals need to digest food to provide energy. Energy is lost from the animal's body in the following way.

* Metabolism.
* Excretion (urine or sweat).
* Exercise.
* The production of heat.
* The production of faeces.
* Combating illness.

> **METABOLISM**
> The chemical reactions that occur in an animal's body.

Dental formula

Dental formula is the arrangement and number of teeth in the mouth of an animal. This formula will indicate whether the animal is a herbivore, omnivore or carnivore.

> **CARNIVORE**
> Eats meat only.
>
> **HERBIVORE**
> Eats plants only.
>
> **OMNIVORE**
> Eats both plants and animals.

The dental formula of cattle and sheep is:

I C P M

0 0 3 3 (upper jaw)
—————————
4 0 3 3 (lower jaw)

The dental formula of a pig is:

I C P M

3 1 4 3 (upper jaw)
—————————
3 1 4 3 (lower jaw)

> **I**: incisors.
> **C**: canines.
> **P**: premolars.
> **M**: molars.

THE DIGESTION OF FOOD TAKES PLACE IN FIVE STAGES	
1. Ingestion	• Food entering the mouth.
2. Digestion	• The breakdown of food into small pieces. • Food is digested mechanically using the teeth and the muscular contractions of the digestive system. • Food is digested chemically by the enzymes.
3. Absorption	• Digested food enters the bloodstream.
4. Assimilation	• Using the absorbed food for various processes in the body.
5. Egestion	• Getting rid of undigested and unabsorbed food.

> **PERISTALSIS**
> The wave like muscular contractions of
> the walls of the digestive system.

PARTS OF THE DIGESTIVE SYSTEM AND THE DIGESTION OF FOOD	
Mouth	• Food enters and is broken down physically. • Food is mixed with saliva. • Mucus in the salvia lubricates the food and aids chewing. • Salvia also contains the enzyme salivary amylase. • Salivary amylase begins the breakdown of starch by converting it to maltose.
Stomach	• **Monogastric animals:** Animals that have one stomach, e.g. pigs, humans.
Ruminant animals	• Animals which have a four-chambered stomach, e.g. cows, sheep.

The ruminant stomach

Rumen

The rumen is the first and largest chamber. The main function of the rumen is to allow high fibrous food to be digested. Bacteria and protozoans are found in the rumen and digest cellulose. These bacteria also synthesis amino acids and B vitamins for the animal.

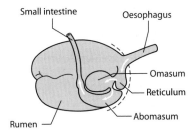

Reticulum

The reticulum helps bring food from the rumen back to the mouth for rumination. This process is commonly referred to as 'chewing the cud'.

Fig. 7.1 The ruminant stomach.

Omasum

The omasum is the third chamber. When food is reswallowed following rumination, it enters this chamber. Here, food is squeezed and water is reabsorbed.

Abomasum

The abomasum is the true stomach.

Digestive enzymes are secreted and digestion is completed here.

* In the young calf or lamb, the first three chambers are not fully developed. As a result of this, when the young animal is suckling, the milk is delivered directly to the abomasum.

* The abomasum is known as the **oesophageal groove**: A groove in the wall of the rumen is stimulated by the young animal suckling and forms a tube to direct milk from the oesophagus to the abomasum.

* The enzyme pepsin found in the stomach/abomasum breaks down proteins to peptides.

* Rennin in the abomasum curdles the milk.

The small intestine

Duodenum

The first part of the small intestine is the duodenum. The pancreas secretes pancreatic juice into the duodenum.

Pancreatic juice contains:

* Trypsin: Breaks down proteins to peptides.

* Amylase: Breaks down starch to maltose.

* Lipase: Breaks down lipids to fatty acids and glycerol.

The walls of the small intestine produce intestinal juices.

Intestinal juices contains:

* Maltase: Breaks down maltose to glucose.

* Sucrase: Breaks down sucrose to glucose.

* Lactase: Breaks down lactose to glucose.

* Erepsin: Breaks down proteins and peptides to amino acids.

Liver

* The liver produces bile which emulsifies fats.

* Bile is made in the liver and stored in the gall-bladder.

FUNCTIONS OF THE LIVER
* Regulates the amount of fats, carbohydrates and proteins in the body.
* Produces bile which breaks down fat during digestion.
* Involved in heat production.
* Stores vitamins and minerals.
* Stores glycogen – changes it into sugar when levels are low.

> ### FUNCTIONS OF THE LIVER (CONTINUED)
> - Breaks down excess proteins (deamination).
> - Detoxifies poisons.
> - Breaks down red blood cells.
> - Involved in the assimilation of digested food.

Ileum

The second part of the small intestine is the Ileum. The end products of digestion are absorbed through the intestinal wall into the bloodstream and transported to the liver via the hepatic portal vein.

* Carbohydrates $\rightarrow$ glucose.

* Proteins $\rightarrow$ amino acids.

* Fats $\rightarrow$ fatty acids and glycerol.

Fatty acids and glycerol enter lacteals, which are branches of the lymphatic system.

> ### VILLI
> Folds in the wall of the small intestine.
> These increase the surface area for the absorption of digested food.

The large intestine

The large intestine is made up of the caecum, colon, rectum and anus.

The functions of the large intestine

* Egestion of the waste products of the digestive system.

* Reabsorption of water into the bloodstream.

The digestive system in poultry

Crop

The part of the digestive system near the throat where food is stored prior to digestion.

Proventriculus

The first part of the stomach is the proventriculus. It stores and starts to digest food before it enters the gizzard.

Gizzard

The second part of the stomach is the gizzard. Poultry swallow grit and pass it into the gizzard. Because poultry have no teeth, they use the grit to grind hard foods such as cereal grains.

THE DIET OF RUMINANTS VERSES THE DIET OF NON-RUMINANTS	
RUMINANTS	NON-RUMINANTS
• Diet is high in fibre. • Eat grass, silage, hay and some concentrates. • Are not fed a wide range of minerals and vitamins. • Are given a less varied diet. • Are fed crude protein.	• Diet is low in fibre. • Eat a balanced ration. • Are fed minerals and vitamins. • Are given a varied diet. • Are fed high-quality protein, especially lysine.

COMPARING THE DIET OF A COW WITH THAT OF A CALF	
CALF	COW
• First fed colostrum, then fed milk. • Has a high protein diet. • Is fed minerals and vitamins. • Is given access to hay and concentrates which encourages the 'scratch factor'. • Can be weaned onto water at about six weeks, then are put out to grass.	• Has a low protein diet. • Eats high fibre food – grass, hay, silage. • Is fed minerals.

The 'scratch factor'

The scratch factor is the introduction of bacteria and protozoans into the rumen of the young calf/lamb. Calves/lambs are born without these bacteria and protozoans in their rumen. This is achieved by giving the young animals access to hay and concentrates.

The circulatory system

The circulatory system consists of the heart, blood and blood vessels. The heart is made up of four chambers: left ventricle, right ventricle, left atrium, right atrium.

Blood

The blood consists of red blood cells, white blood cells, platelets, plasma.

PARTS OF THE BLOOD	
Red blood cells	• Carry oxygen around the body. • Contain the pigment haemoglobin, which binds to the oxygen.
White blood cells	• Help the body to fight infection.
Platelets	• Help to clot the blood.
Plasma	• The liquid part of the blood. • Carries dissolved substances around the body.

BLOOD VESSELS	
Arteries	• Carry blood away from the heart.
Veins	• Carry blood towards the heart.
Capillaries	• Substances enter and leave the blood through the walls of the capillaries.

The steps involved in the clotting of blood

1. When platelets are exposed to air, prothrombin is converted to thrombin with the help of calcium and vitamin K.

2. Once thrombin is detected in the blood, soluble fibrinogen is converted into insoluble fibrin.

3. The fibrin forms a fine network of threads in which the blood cells are trapped. This leads to the formation of a scab.

The functions of the circulatory system

* Carries digested food.

* Carries oxygen.

* Distributes heat.

* Carries white blood cells and antibodies.

* Carries waste products to the kidneys.

* Carries hormones from the gland to the target organ.

The lymphatic system

Mammals have a secondary circulatory system called the lymphatic system.

The functions of the lymphatic system

* Collects fluid, which surrounds all the cells in the body.

* Helps defend the body against disease-causing organisms.

* Absorbs and transports fats from the digestive system.

Lymph nodes

Lymph nodes are swellings found along the lymph vessels in the neck, under the arm and groin. Lymph nodes filter bacteria and store white blood cells.

The nervous system

The basic unit of nerve tissue is the neuron.

The function of the nervous system

To enable the organism to respond to changes in its environment.

The pathway of a nervous message

1. A stimulus is detected by one of the sensory organs.
2. An electric message is sent to the brain via a sensory nerve.
3. This message is then compared to stored information.
4. A response is sent via a motor nerve.
5. This results in muscle action.

> The sensory organs are: ear (hearing), eye (sight), nose (smell), skin (touch) and tongue (taste).

The two nervous systems

1. **Central Nervous System (CNS):** Consists of the brain and spinal cord.
2. **Peripheral Nervous System (PNS):** All the nerves outside the CNS.

The endocrine system

The endocrine system controls certain organs in the body by sending chemical messengers (hormones) through the bloodstream to these organs. The hormones are produced in various parts of the body and released directly into the bloodstream. This system is much slower than the nervous system, but the effects last much longer.

GLAND	LOCATION AND HORMONE PRODUCED	FUNCTION
Pituitary	• Brain. • Master gland.	• Produces hormones which control the other endocrine glands.
Thyroid	• Neck. • Thyroxin.	• Controls the rate of growth and development.
Adrenal	• Above the kidneys. • Adrenaline.	• Prepares the body for action.
Pancreas	• Pancreas. • Insulin.	• Controls the blood sugar levels.
Testis	• Testis. • Testosterone.	• Develops the secondary sexual characteristics.
Ovary	• Ovary. • Oestrogen and Progesterone.	• **Oestrogen:** Develops the secondary sexual characteristics and builds up the lining of the womb. • **Progesterone:** Maintains the lining of the womb during early pregnancy.

DIFFERENCES BETWEEN THE NERVOUS AND ENDOCRINE SYSTEMS	
NERVOUS SYSTEM	**ENDOCRINE SYSTEM**
• Response is fast-acting. • Consists of electrical messages. • Response is short-lived.	• Response is slow-acting. • Consists of chemical messages. • Response is long-lasting.

The skeleton system

The functions of the skeleton

* Protection.
* Movement.
* Support.

Bone matter

* **Living material:** nerves, cells, blood vessels.
* **Mineral material:** calcium phosphate, calcium carbonate.

Muscle (also referred to as flesh or lean meat)

* **Striped muscle:** Attached to the skeleton – under voluntary control.
* **Smooth muscle:** Around inner organs, e.g. in the wall of the stomach, around blood vessels – under involuntary control.
* **Cardiac muscle:** Found only in the heart – under involuntary control.

There are five types of joints

1. Hinge joint.
2. Pivot joint.
3. Ball and socket joint.
4. Fixed joint.
5. Gliding joint.

The immune system

The functions of the immune system

* Protects the body from disease or disease-causing organisms.
* Helps the body to overcome an infection or disease.

Immunity

Immunity is the ability to resist or overcome disease.

* **Active immunity:** Active immunity is acquired by suffering from the disease and the body produces its own antibodies, or the animal is vaccinated.
* **Passive immunity:** The body doesn't make its own antibodies. Passive immunity is acquired by taking antibiotics or by feeding young animals colostrum (beastings).

The respiratory system

The parts of the breathing system

* The larynx or voice box.
* The trachea or windpipe.
* The bronchi.
* The bronchioles.

* The alveoli or air sacs.
* The lungs.
* The diaphragm.
* The ribs.

Breathing actions

* **Inspiration:** The taking of air into the lungs.
  - **Medulla oblongata:** An area in the brain that detects the level of carbon dioxide in the blood. When there is an increase in the level of carbon dioxide, a message is sent to the intercostal muscles and the diaphragm to breathe in.
* **Expiration:** The release of air from the lungs.

The urinary system

The parts of the urinary system

* Two kidneys.
* Two ureters.

* The bladder.
* The urethra.

The internal structure of the kidney

* The cortex.
* The Nephron.
* The Bowman's capsule.

* The Loop of Henle.
* The medulla.
* The pelvis.

The functions of the kidney

* Excretes water, salts and urea.
* Controls the water and salt concentration of the blood.
* Reabsorbs wanted minerals and water.

The reproductive system

> **GONADS**
> The general term for the testes and ovaries.

The parts of the male reproductive system

* Testes.
* Penis.
* Epididymis.
* Scrotum.
* Urethra.
* Cowper's gland.
* Prostate gland.
* Seminal vesicle.
* Sperm duct.

Epididymis: Sperm cells mature here and are stored for up to six weeks.

Cowper's gland, prostate gland and seminal vesicle: These produce a liquid called seminal fluid. This fluid is added to sperm cells to form semen.

Hormones in the male reproductive system

* **Testosterone:** Causes the development of the primary and secondary male sex characteristics.
* **FSH (Follicle Stimulating Hormone):** Causes the production of sperm cells.
* **LH (Luteinising Hormone):** Stimulates the testes to produce testosterone.

The parts of the female reproductive system

* Ovaries.
* Fallopian tubes.
* Uterus.
* Cervix.
* Birth canal (vagina).

Ovulation and pregnancy

* An egg is released from the ovary and enters the fallopian tube.

* The egg leaves the ovaries and travels along the fallopian tube.

* Fertilisation occurs in the fallopian tube.

* The fertilised egg then travels to the uterus where implantation occurs.

* The fertilised egg multiplies to become an embryo.

* After some time, the embryo is then referred to as a foetus.

OVULATION
The release of an egg from the ovary.

FERTILISATION
The fusion of an egg cell with a sperm cell, it occurs in the fallopian tube.

IMPLANTATION
When the embryo attaches itself to the lining of the womb wall.

Gestation period

The period of time from conception to birth.

* Cows: 9½ months.

* Sheep: 5 months.

* Sows: 3 months, 3 weeks and 3 days.

Placenta: This acts as a link between the mother's bloodstream and that of the developing foetus.

Umbilical cord: The placenta is attached to the foetus by the umbilical cord.

Amniotic fluid: The fluid which surrounds and protects the embryo in the womb; it acts as a 'shock absorber'.

The oestrus cycle

* When not pregnant, cows and sows come into heat (oestrus) every 21 days.

* Occurs every 16 days in sheep but only in the autumn and winter.

* They release the hormone oestrogen.

* Towards the end of oestrus, an egg is released from the ovary.

* Oestrus lasts for 18 hours in cows, 24–36 hours in sheep and 2–3 days in sows.

8 Plant physiology

Plants are made up of cells (*see* Chapter 10, page 109).

Groups of plant cells that perform a specific function are known as plant tissues.

PLANT TISSUES	
Epidermal tissue	• Allows substances into and out of the plant. • No chloroplasts present, except in the guard cells.
Parenchyma	• The photosynthetic tissue. • Examples are the palisade layer and spongy mesophyll in the leaf.
Transport tissue	• The xylem and phloem. • These tubes move substances around the plant.
Meristem	• The areas of active cell division in the plant. • Found at the growing tips of the roots and shoots.
Collenchyma	• Provides support for the plant.
Schlerenchyma	• Provides support for the plant.
Storage tissue	• Fleshy cells where food is stored.

Parts of the plant

The flower

> **CALYX**
> Formed by the sepals.
>
> **COROLLA**
> Formed by the petals.

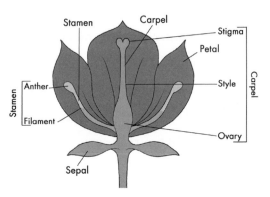

Fig. 8.1 The insect-pollinated flower.

How the flower is suited to insect-pollination

* Colourful petal.

* Nectary contains nectar.

* Produces a scent.

* Produces a small amount of pollen.

* The pollen grains are sticky.

* Anthers and stigma are found inside the flower.

How the flower is suited to wind-pollination

* No energy is wasted producing petals, etc.

* Produces a large amount of pollen.

* The pollen grains are light.

* Stamens hang outside the flower.

* Stigmas are feathery to trap the pollen grains.

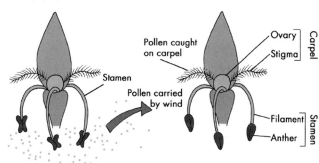

Grass flowers make lots of pollen

Fig. 8.2 The wind-pollinated flower.

The stem

The functions of the stem

* Connects the roots to the leaves, flowers and fruit.

* Holds the plant upright.

* Stores food in some plants.

* Transports water and minerals up from the roots.

* Transports manufactured food from the leaves.

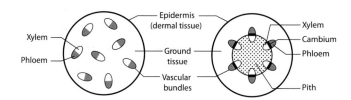

Fig. 8.3 The cross-section of a monocot stem (left) and dicot stem (right).

The root

The functions of the root

* ✱ Anchors the plant in the ground.
* ✱ Absorbs water and minerals from the soil.
* ✱ Stores food in some plants.
* ✱ Involved in vegetative propagation in some plants.

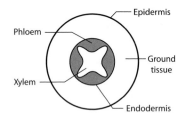

Fig. 8.4 The cross-section of a root.

> **TAPROOT**
> Found in dicots.
>
> **FIBROUS ROOT**
> Found in monocots.

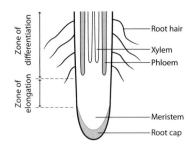

Fig. 8.5 The longitudinal section of a root.

> **ROOT HAIRS**
> Found on all roots, they increase the surface area for the absorption of water and minerals.

The absorption of water and minerals through the root

Water is absorbed from the soil by osmosis. Osmosis is the movement of water from an area of high concentration to an area of low concentration. Minerals dissolved in the soil water enter the plant by active transport. Energy is required to pull the minerals from the soil and into the plant.

> **ACTIVE TRANSPORT**
> The movement of substances from an area of low concentration to an area of high concentration.

The leaf

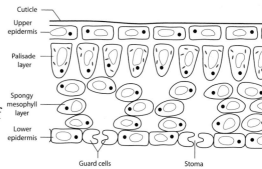

The functions of the leaf

* Photosynthesis.

* Transpiration.

* Allows gases to pass in and out of the plant.

* Stores food in some plants.

The structure of the leaf

Fig. 8.6 The cross-section of a leaf.

* **Cuticle and the upper epidermis:** These layers protect the leaf. They are transparent and allow light into the leaf.

* **Palisade:** Contains a large number of chloroplasts. These absorb light and use the energy for photosynthesis.

* **Spongy mesophyll:** Allows oxygen and carbon dioxide to move around the leaf.

* **Lower epidermis:** Contains stomata and guard cells.

* **Stomata:** Oxygen and carbon dioxide enter and exit the leaf through these.

Photosynthesis

Photosynthesis is the ability of green plants to make their own food. It occurs in the chloroplasts of the cell. In the presence of sunlight and chlorophyll, plants convert carbon dioxide and water into glucose and oxygen.

$$CO_2 + H_2O \xrightarrow[\text{chlorophyll}]{\text{light}} Glucose + O_2$$

What happens to the oxygen?

* Released out through the stomata and into the atmosphere.

* Used by the plant for respiration.

What happens to the glucose?

* Can be converted to starch and stored.

* Can be converted to cellulose and used to make new cell walls.

* Can be combined with nitrogen and other minerals.

* Can be used in respiration.

How is the structure of the leaf adapted for photosynthesis?

* Flattened for large surface area.

* Thin for maximum diffusion of carbon dioxide into the cells.

* Stomata for entry of carbon dioxide and exit of oxygen.

* Guard cells to close the stomata in darkness and open them in light.

* Air spaces in the spongy mesophyll for the movement of carbon dioxide and water within the leaf.

* Xylem vessels to bring water and phloem tubes to take away glucose.

Transpiration and translocation

Transpiration

The loss of water vapour from the surface of the plant. The water vapour passes out through the stomata.

The transpiration stream

The flow of water through the plant, from the root to the stomata in the leaf.

Benefits of the transpiration stream

✓ The transpiration stream brings water to the leaves for photosynthesis.

✓ The water helps to maintain turgor in the plant cells.

✓ The water brings minerals to the cells.

✓ The evaporation of the water from the leaves cools them down.

Factors affecting the rate of transpiration

* Humidity of the air.

* Temperature.

* Air movements.

* Light intensity.

* Water content of the soil.

* Total leaf area.

* Number of stomata.

> Water moves **up** through the xylem tubes.
> Food moves **up and down** through the phloem tubes.

WHY POTTED PLANTS LOSE TURGIDITY ON A VERY WARM DAY

There is limited amount of water in potted plants. Plants lose a lot of water through transpiration. Transpiration increases with temperature. Plants need water to retain turgidity.

Translocation

The movement of food from one location to another. Food is produced by photosynthesis. It is moved either to storage sites or to areas of rapid growth.

Plant tropisms

A plant's response to a stimulus.

* **Phototropism:** A plant's response to light.

* **Geotropism:** A plant's response to gravity.

* **Hydrotropism:** A plant's response to water.

* **Thigmotropism:** A plant's response to touch.

* **Chemotropism:** A plant's response to chemicals.

POSITIVE RESPONSE
Plant grows towards the stimulus.

NEGATIVE RESPONSE
Plant grows away from the stimulus.

Fig. 8.7 Tendrils.

Modified stems, roots and leaves

Various parts of plants have been modified over time. Often the storage modifications are associated with the lifespan of the plant. The modifications are for food storage or vegetative propagation.

TYPES OF PLANTS	
Annuals	• Complete their life cycle in one year. • Grow from seed; produce leaves, flowers and seeds; and die. • Examples are cereals and groundsel.
Biennials	• Complete their life cycle in two growing seasons. • Grow in one season and store food. • In the second year, they flower and produce seeds. • Are harvested at the end of the first year. • Examples are sugarbeet and carrot.
Perennials	• Live for many years. • Examples are daisy, grasses, oak, ash and roses.

MODIFIED STEMS	
Corms	• A short vertical underground stem which swells with stored food. • This stored food is used for new growth the following year. • Examples are crocus and gladiolas.
Tubers	• Potato plants produce an underground stem system. • The ends of these stems become swollen and store food. • An example is potatoes.
Runners	• Stems grow horizontally above the ground. • Buds develop along the stem. • These buds develop their own root and shoot system and form new plants. • An example is strawberries.
Rhizomes	• Underground stems which grow horizontally. • The stems store food and are involved in vegetative propagation. • An example is scutch grass.

MODIFIED LEAVES	
Bulbs	• Leaves become swollen and fleshy with stored food. • Examples are onion, daffodil and tulip.

MODIFIED ROOTS	
Root tubers	• When fibrous roots become swollen with food reserves. • An example is dahlia.
Tap root	• Stores food for the plant. • Anchors the plant in the soil. • Able to absorb water and minerals from deeper in the soil. • Examples are sugarbeet and carrot.

Note: Do not confuse stem tubers with root tubers.

MODIFICATIONS FOR PROTECTION	
Protection from being eaten	• Thorns. • Chemical forms of protection, e.g. poisons. • Stinging glands, e.g. nettles.
Protection against water loss	• Desert plants reduce their leaves to non-transpiring thorns.

Reproduction in the flowering plant

Sexual reproduction

1. Pollination

The transfer of pollen from the anther to the stigma.

There are two types of pollination.

1. **Self-pollination:** The transfer of pollen from an anther to a stigma on the same plant.

2. **Cross-pollination:** The transfer of pollen from an anther to a stigma on a different plant.

THE TWO METHODS OF POLLINATION	
Wind pollination	The pollen is transferred in the wind.
Insect pollination	The pollen is transferred by insects.

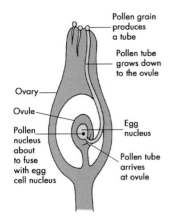

Pollen grain produces a tube

Pollen tube grows down to the ovule

Ovary

Ovule

Pollen nucleus about to fuse with egg cell nucleus

Egg nucleus

Pollen tube arrives at ovule

2. Fertilisation

The fusion of the pollen and egg.

1. When a pollen grain lands on the stigma, it grows a pollen tube down through the style into the ovary towards the egg.

2. The nucleus of the pollen and the nucleus of the egg fuse, and the egg is fertilised.

3. The fertilised egg grows into a seed.

Fig. 8.8 Fusion of the pollen and egg.

3. Seed dispersal

Scattering the seeds away from the parent plant.

Importance of seed dispersal

*   Prevents the new plant competing with the parent plant.
*   Avoids overcrowding.
*   Allows plants to colonise new areas.

METHODS OF SEED DISPERSAL	
Wind dispersal	• Parachute fruits of dandelions. • Winged fruits of ash and sycamore.
Animal dispersal	• Birds and animals eat fruits and the undigested seed are dropped elsewhere in the faeces. • Hooks on the fruits get entangled in the fur of animals.

Self-dispersal	• Members of the legume family have pods, which burst open when ripe and throw their seeds a few feet away.
Water dispersal	• Seeds have a spongy covering which makes them buoyant.

4. Germination

The development of a seed into a seedling.

There are two kinds depending on whether or not the cotyledons come above the ground to photosynthesise.

1. **Epigeal germination:** The cotyledons come **above** the ground and photosynthesise.

2. **Hypogeal germination:** The cotyledons remain **below** the ground.

Environmental factors necessary for germination

* **Water:** Required to hydrate the seed and provide a medium for chemical reactions to occur.

* **Oxygen:** Required for aerobic respiration and the release of energy.

* **Temperature:** Enzymes control germination and the rate of their action is controlled by temperature.

Asexual reproduction (vegetative propagation)

NATURAL METHODS	
Layering	• When a branch touches the ground and grows roots from the area of contact. • The plant is later severed from the parent plant and becomes an independent plant. • An example is blackberries.
Runners	• Buds develop along the stem and develop into new plants. • An example is strawberries.

ARTIFICIAL METHODS		
Mound layering	• A low flexible branch is pinned to the ground and covered with soil. • When the area of contact produces roots, the plant is severed from the parent plant.	 *Fig. 8.9 Mound layering.*
Air layering	• When the branches are not flexible, a bag of soil is tied around the branch. • Roots form in the area covered by the bag and the plant is severed from the parent plant.	 *Fig. 8.10 Air layering.*
Cuttings	• A young stem is cut just below a node and dipped in rooting hormone. • The stem is potted in free draining, well-watered compost. • The pot is covered with a plastic bag to reduce transpiration.	
Grafting	• The root stock has its stem removed and is cut in a V. • The stem of a scion is cut to fit the V of the rootstock. • The scion and rootstock are joined together. • The cut surface is sealed with wax to exclude micro-organisms. • The layers unite to form a new xylem and phloem to connect stock and scion.	 *Fig. 8.11 Grafting.*
Micro-propagation	• Large numbers of plants are grown from small pieces of plant tissue (*see* Chapter 12, Experiment 16, page 132).	

SEXUAL REPRODUCTION VERSUS ASEXUAL REPRODUCTION	
SEXUAL REPRODUCTION	**VEGETATIVE REPRODUCTION**
• Allows for variation. • Number of offspring depends on the number of seeds produced and germinated. • Takes a long time for seeds to be produced. • Is a complicated process.	• Plants are identical to parents. • Large number of offspring can be produced. • Is a relatively quick process. • Is a simple process.

Plant hormones

There are four main naturally occurring hormones:

1. Auxin	• Controls cell elongation. • Controls root and fruit formation. • Controls the priority of the main shoot over lateral shoots (apical dominance). • Causes plants to grow towards light.
2. Ethane	• Involved in the ripening of fruit. • Causes leaves to fall in autumn.
3. Giberellin	• Stimulates the germination of seeds. • Starts the growth of dormant buds.
4. Cytokinin	• Increases the rate of cell division.

The uses of hormones

* Used in some weed killers.

* Used as a dwarfing agent.

* Used in rooting hormone powder.

* Used in the production of seedless fruit.

* Used in micro-propagation.

* Control apical dominance in plants.

* Are involved in plant tropisms.

* Ethane encourages fruit to ripen.

9 Forestry

The trees used in commercial forestry are conifers. This is because they have a fast growth rate and they grow satisfactorily on poor soils. The two most common trees planted are Sitka Spruce and Lodgepole Pine.

Steps involved in planting forestry

1. The area is properly fenced off.

2. If the land is wet, it will have to be drained.

3. The trees are sat 2 m apart.

4. If the land is drained, the trees are planted on the mounds of earth.

5. On undrained land, they are simply planted in the ground.

6. The trees are fertilised using ground rock phosphate.

Fig. 9.1 A felled tree.

7. After 18–20 years, thinning is carried out.

8. Final harvest or clear felling is the total clearance of trees from the area. This is the most valuable timber.

9. Once the trees are removed, stump clearance occurs: This is chemically treating the stumps to make them decay quickly.

Fertiliser requirements of forest trees

Trees only require a small quantity of nutrients. Most soils have sufficient nutrients to meet their requirements. Minerals are released from the parent rock material by chemical and biological weathering. Bacteria and other soil organisms release nutrients from humus and other organic matter. The soil pH affects the availability of phosphorus. At a pH of less that 5.5, phosphorus forms an insoluble compound, therefore making it unavailable

Fig. 9.2 The stump of a tree remaining after final harvest.

for the trees to absorb. For this reason, the straight fertiliser (*see* page 123) ground rock phosphate is applied. The fertiliser is applied at a rate of 100 g/tree or 250 kg/ha.

The importance of thinning

The poorest trees are removed leaving the better quality trees. This encourages the growth of the better quality trees. These remaining trees grow at an increased rate due to the reduced competition for water, nutrients and space. The trees removed are used to make cheap timber products, i.e. chipboard and fibreboard.

Fig. 9.3 Trees prior to thinning.

Why trees are planted 2 m apart

* Planting the trees close together allows for a higher degree of selection. The better trees grow well at the expense of the poorer trees.

* Close planting encourages trees to grow tall and straight as they compete for light. This reduces the number of branches produced and therefore reduces the number of knots in the timber.

Fig. 9.4 Recently planted trees.

10 Genetics

Genetics is the study of how traits are inherited.

Chromosomes

Chromosomes are long DNA molecules containing genetic information (genes). Each individual has a pair of similar chromosomes called a homologous pair. This is referred to as the diploid condition (2n). Egg and sperm (egg and pollen) cells however, have only half the number of chromosomes. This is known as the haploid condition (n).

The cell

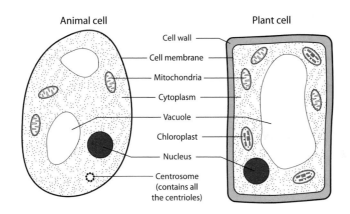

Fig. 10.1 Animal cell (left) and plant cell (right).

CELL ORGANELLES AND THEIR FUNCTION	
Cell wall	Gives strength and support to the plant cell.
Cell membrane	A thin skin that controls what substances enter and leave the cell.
Vacuole	Used for storage.

Plastids	Only found in plant cells. There are three types of plastid. • **Chloroplast:** Contains a green pigment, chlorophyll. • **Chromoplast:** Contains red, yellow and orange pigments. Found in the petals. • **Leucoplast:** Colourless. They are used to store starch.
Nucleus	Controls all the activities of the cell.
Cytoplasm	A jelly-like substance in which all the cell organelles are suspended.
Mitrochondria	Supply energy for the cell.
Centriole	Found in animal cells only. Involved in cell division.
Centrosome	Area in the animal cell where the centrioles are located.

A **stain** can be used to make cells more visible under the microscope. Examples of stains that can be used are iodine, methylene blue and potassium iodide.

The differences between plant and animal cells

PLANT CELL	ANIMAL CELL
• Cellulose cell wall. • Chlorophyll. • Plastids present. • No centrosome. • One large vacuole.	• No cellulose cell wall. • No chlorophyll. • No plastids present. • Centrosome present. • Many small vacuoles.

There are two types of cell division – mitosis and meiosis

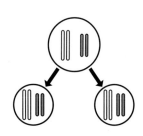

Fig. 10.2 Mitosis.

Mitosis is when a cell divides into two.

* Each daughter cell has the same number of chromosomes as the parent cell.

* Each daughter cell is identical to the parent cell.

* Mitosis occurs in the somatic cells.

* Mitosis results in the growth of plants and animals.

Meiosis is when a cell divides into four.

* The daughter cells have half the number of chromosomes of the parent cell.

* The daughter cells are not identical to the parent cell.

* Meiosis results in the production of the sex cells.

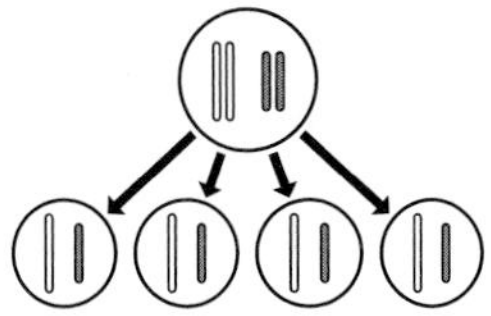

Fig. 10.3 Meiosis.

The importance of meiosis in reproduction

* Meiosis reduces or halves the chromosome number.

* It produces haploid (n) cells, i.e. the gametes.

* Crossing over during meiosis produces variation.

* The diploid (2n) state is restored at fertilisation.

A more detailed look at mitosis

Mitosis: This can be divided into five phases.

1. Interphase

The cell prepares for division – the cell organelles duplicate.

Fig. 10.4 Interphase.

2. Prophase

Chromosomes shorten and thicken and become visible under the microscope. Each one doubles itself and is now made up of two identical chromatids, held together by a centromere. The nuclear membrane dissolves and the chromosomes are now suspended in the cytoplasm of the cell.

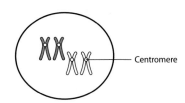

Centromere

Fig. 10.5 Prophase.

3. Metaphase

Spindle fibres form between the two poles of the cell. The chromosomes attach themselves to the spindle at the equator.

In animal cells, the spindle fibres are formed by the centrides. In plant cells, they are formed from the cytoplasm.

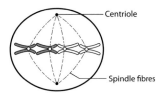

Centriole

Spindle fibres

Fig. 10.6 Metaphase.

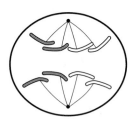

4. Anaphase

The chromatids separate at the centromere and one of each pair migrates on the spindle to each of the two poles.

Fig. 10.7 Anaphase.

5. Telophase

When all the chromatids (now chromosomes) have collected around the two poles, a nuclear membrane forms around each group. The cytoplasm in the cell begins to divide at the equator and two new cells are formed.

Fig. 10.8 Telophase.

Genetic crosses

Genetic crosses are used to determine the characteristics of the offspring when two plants or animals are crossed.

Some terms required for these crosses:

* **Alleles:** Different forms of the same gene.
* **Homozygous dominant:** When the two dominant genes are present, e.g. AA.
* **Homozygous recessive:** When the two recessive genes are present, e.g. aa.
* **Heterozygous:** When one dominant and one recessive gene are present, e.g. Aa.
* **Incomplete dominance:** In the heterozygous condition, neither gene is completely dominant over the other, e.g. A red flower crossed with a white flower produces a pink flower; a red coat crossed with a white coat produces a roan coat.
* **9 : 3 : 3 : 1:** Ratio of offspring produced in a dihybrid cross when two parents, heterozygous for both characteristics, are crossed.
* **Genotype:** The letters used to describe the genetic make up of the organism.
* **Phenotype:** The physical appearance of the organism.
* **Gamete:** The sex cell.
* **Gonads:** The reproductive organs in animals.

* **Haploid:** Having half the chromosome number – one set of chromosomes, e.g. 23 in humans.

* **Diploid:** Having two sets of chromosomes, e.g. 46 in humans.

Monohybrid cross

A monohybrid cross is a cross which deals with one trait.

* In fruit flies, long wing (L) is dominant over short wing (l). Indicate the genotype and phenotype of the offspring resulting from a cross between a homozygous dominant fly and a homozyous recessive fly.

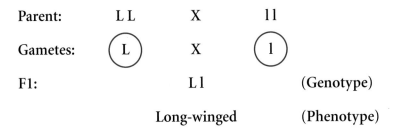

Parent: L L   X   l l

Gametes: (L)   X   (l)

F1:   L l   (Genotype)

                    Long-winged   (Phenotype)

* In pigs, curly tail (C) is dominant over straight tail (c). Indicate the genotype and phenotype of the offspring resulting from a cross between two pigs, both heterozygous for curly tail.

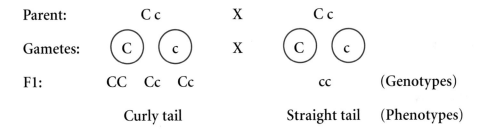

Parent: C c   X   C c

Gametes: (C) (c)   X   (C) (c)

F1:   CC   Cc   Cc   cc   (Genotypes)

                   Curly tail   Straight tail   (Phenotypes)

Incomplete dominance

* A bull homozygous for red colour (RR) is crossed with a cow homozygous for white colour (rr). The offspring (F1) are heterozygous for roan colour. Outline this cross using a diagram.

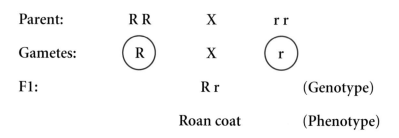

Parent: R R   X   r r

Gametes: (R)   X   (r)

F1:   R r   (Genotype)

                     Roan coat   (Phenotype)

* In sweet pea plants, red petals (R) are dominant over white petals (r). Indicate the genotype and phenotype of the plants resulting from a cross between a homozygous red flower plant and a heterozygous red flower plant.

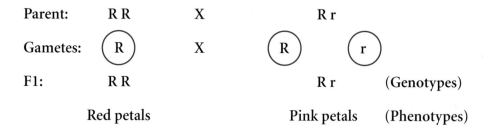

Parent: R R   X   R r

Gametes: (R)   X   (R)   (r)

F1:   R R   R r   (Genotypes)

             Red petals   Pink petals   (Phenotypes)

Dihybrid cross

A dihybrid cross is a cross which deals with two traits.

* In pea plants, tall plant (T) is dominant over short plant (t). Also yellow pod colour (Y) is dominant over green pod colour (y). Show how the genotypes and phenotypes of the F1 progeny for a cross involving a tall plant with yellow pods (heterozygous for both traits) and a short plant with green pods.

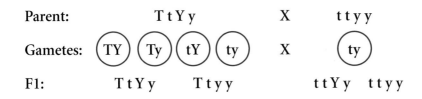

Parent: T t Y y   X   t t y y

Gametes: (TY) (Ty) (tY) (ty)   X   (ty)

F1:   T t Y y   T t y y   t t Y y   t t y y

Genotypes	Phenotypes
T t Y y	Tall with yellow pods.
T t y y	Tall with green pods.
t t Y y	Short with yellow pods.
t t y y	Short with green pods.

* Outline a cross where both plants are tall with yellow pods and heterozygous for both characteristics.

Parent: T t Y y   X   T t Y y

Gametes: (TY) (Ty) (tY) (ty)   X   (TY) (Ty) (tY) (ty)

Use a Punnet square to work out all the possible combinations at fertilisation.

	TY	**Ty**	**tY**	**ty**
TY	TTYY Tall and yellow pods.	TTYy Tall and yellow pods.	TtYY Tall and yellow pods.	TtYy Tall and yellow pods.
Ty	TTYy Tall and yellow pods.	TTyy Tall and green pods.	TtYy Tall and yellow pods.	Ttyy Tall and green pods.
tY	TtYY Tall and yellow pods.	TtYy Tall and yellow pods.	ttYY Short and yellow pods.	ttYy Short and yellow pods.
ty	TtYy Tall and yellow pods.	Ttyy Tall and green pods.	ttYy Short and yellow pods.	ttyy Short and green pods.

Ratio of phenotypes: 9: Tall with yellow pods.

3: Tall with green pods.

3: Short with yellow pods.

1: Short with green pods.

---

9 : 3 : 3 : 1

In a dihybrid cross, when crossing two organisms that are heterozygous for both characteristics, the ratio of the phenotypes is always 9: 3: 3: 1.

- 9: Dominant characteristic and dominant characteristic.
- 3: Dominant characteristic and recessive characteristic.
- 3: Recessive characteristic and dominant characteristic.
- 1: Recessive characteristic and recessive characteristic.

Mendel and inheritance

Mendel studied the inheritance of characteristics in pea plants.

Pea plants

The reasons he chose pea plants were:

* They grow quickly and the results can be seen in the same growing season.

* In nature, pea plants are self-pollinating, but pollination can be controlled by hand and so plants can be cross-pollinated.

Fruit flies (Drosophila)

Fruit flies (Drosophila) are also used in the study of genetics. The reasons for this are:

* Fruit flies are easy to culture in the laboratory.

* They produce a new generation every two weeks.

* Their chromosomes are large.

* They have only four pairs of chromosomes.

* They produce large numbers of offspring.

* Their genetic mutations are well-documented.

Artificial insemination (AI)

Artificial insemination is the most important technique ever devised for the genetic improvement of farm animals.

Adding an extender and the storage of semen

The main reason for extending or diluting semen is to increase the number of females that may be serviced. A good extender not only adds volume to the semen but favours sperm survival and longevity. Semen is usually stored in liquid nitrogen at a temperature of −196 °C. Liquid nitrogen is preferred because there is no evidence of fertility deterioration with age. The liquid nitrogen ensures the mobility and effectiveness of the sperm.

Advantages of artificial insemination

✓ Normally, a bull would be limited to 100 matings per year; with artificial insemination, a bull may provide semen for more than 60,000 services.

✓ Exposure of bulls to infectious genital diseases is prevented.

✓ Semen can be stored for many years.

✓ There is a wide range of sires to choose from.

✓ Artificial insemination increases genetic progress of farm stock.

✓ Artificial insemination results in improving the performance of the offspring.

✓ Artificial insemination increases the chances of fertilization because the sperm is placed directly into the uterus.

✓ The semen can be checked more frequently for quality.

✓ The date of insemination is known; therefore, the date of calving can be estimated.

✓ No need to purchase, house or feed a bull.

✓ Artificial insemination is less dangerous due to eliminating the need for a bull on the farm.

> **SPERM OR SEMEN?**
> - **Sperm**
>   Male gamete.
> - **Semen**
>   Liquid containing the sperm.

Disadvantages of artificial insemination

❖ Timing is critical – insemination must be carried out at the correct time for fertilisation to occur.

❖ Missing heat periods increases the calving interval.

❖ Artificial insemination can be expensive if animals repeat.

❖ Farmers are required to detect when animals are in heat, therefore adding to their workload.

❖ Success or failure depends on how well heat detection is carried out.

> **CALVING INTERVAL**
>
> The length of time between a cow giving birth to one calf and a subsequent calf. Ideally the calving interval should be kept as close to 12 months as possible.

> **TAIL PAINTING**
>
> Tail painting is used to assist the farmer in detecting when animals are in heat.
>
> A strip of paint is applied along the tail area of the cow. This strip should be about 30 cm in length and 7 cm in width. Paint strips should be checked at milking. Cows with some or all the paint removed are almost certainly in heat.

Advantages of having a bull on the farm

✓ The farmer is not required to detect when the animals are in heat.

✓ Repeat services can be carried out at no extra cost.

Disadvantages of having a bull on the farm

❖ Bulls are aggressive and dangerous animals.

❖ Bulls may be difficult to manage.

❖ Maintaining good farm fencing can be expensive.

❖ Bulls may serve heifers not required for breeding.

❖ All offspring will be of the same breed.

Embryo transplantation

Cows with superior characteristics are given hormones to increase the number of eggs released from their ovaries.

1. These eggs are surgically removed.

2. The eggs are fertilised.

3. The fertilised eggs are then implanted into other cows, where they continue to develop. This allows cows to produce more offspring than they could naturally.

Mutations

A spontaneous change in the amount or structure of DNA.

Causes of cell mutations

* X-rays.
* Radiation.
* UV light.
* Sunlight.
* Radon.
* Asbestos.
* Carcinogens.

Performance testing and progeny testing

Performance testing

Keeping records of an animal's individual performance, e.g. growth rate, efficiency and ability to convert feed; and comparing them with the records of other animals kept under similar conditions.

Progeny testing

Comparing records of an animal's offspring with the offspring of other animals kept under similar conditions, e.g. growth rate, efficiency and ability to convert feed.

11 Fertilisers, pollution and the environment

Fertilisers are required for the proper growth and development of crops. The rate at which fertilisers are applied to crops has to be carefully calculated so as to prevent pollution.

Many of the products and by-products produced on the farm may cause severe pollution if not treated or discarded properly.

The carbon cycle

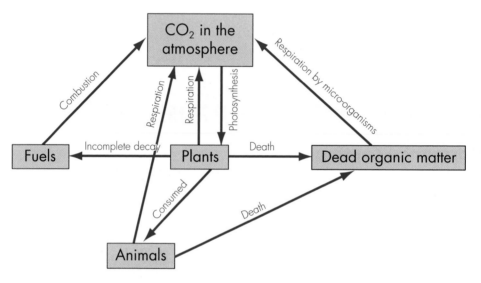

Fig. 11.1 The carbon cycle.

The nitrogen cycle

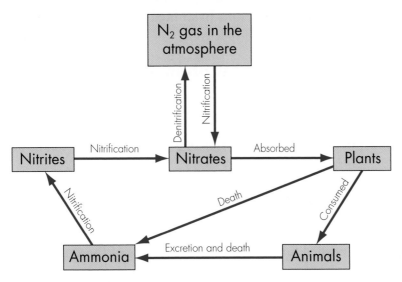

Fig. 11.2 The nitrogen cycle.

Nitrogen, phosphorus and potassium (N, P and K)

The three main nutrients required by plants are nitrogen, phosphorus and potassium.

Why plants need nitrogen

* Nitrogen is needed to make **chlorophyll**. This results in more photosynthesis; therefore, there is more of a yield.

* Nitrogen makes up 16 per cent of protein. It is a constituent of **amino acids**; therefore, it is needed for growth. A deficiency of nitrogen causes stunted growth and chlorosis.

The disadvantages of applying too much nitrogen to a crop

❖ Too much nitrogen fertiliser causes clover to die off.
❖ Leaching or run-off may result in pollution.
❖ Crops are more susceptible to disease.
❖ Too much nitrogen fertiliser delays ripening of cereal crops.
❖ It causes lodging in cereal crops.
❖ Excess nitrogen results in an increase in cost.

Why plants need phosphorus

Phosphorus is required for growth, root development, seed formation and early ripening. A deficiency in phosphorus results in stunted growth, a reduced number of tillers in cereal crops and a purplish tint to leaves.

The difference between 'total phosphates' and 'available phosphates'

* **Total phosphates:** All the phosphates in the soil in all forms.
* **Available phosphates:** The soluble forms of phosphates which can be absorbed by plants.

Why plants need potassium

* Plants require potassium to **make protein.**
* Potassium is also needed for the **opening and closing of the stomata.**
* A deficiency may lead to brown scorching and curling of the leaf tips. A deficiency of potassium may make some plants more prone to frost damage and disease.

How to determine the correct amount of fertiliser to add to a crop

The factors taken into consideration are:

* The soil type.
* The soil's fertility status; determined using a soil test.
* The pH of the soil.
* The type of crop.
* The place in rotation.
* The climate.
* The cost of the fertiliser.
* The requirements of REPS.

How to prevent the run-off of fertilisers

* Do not apply during periods of heavy rainfall.
* Apply the fertiliser at the proper rate.
* Use the correct type of fertiliser.

∗ Apply to the crop during periods of rapid growth.

∗ Keep away from rivers, streams, etc.

A straight fertiliser

A straight fertiliser contains only one of the three minerals: nitrogen, phosphorus and potassium. Some examples of straight fertilisers are: calcium ammonium nitrate (contains only nitrogen), ground rock phosphate (contains only phosphorus) and urea (contains only nitrogen).

A compound fertiliser

A compound fertiliser contains two or all three of the minerals nitrogen, phosphorus and potassium.

Examples are: 10 : 10 : 20 and 0 : 7 : 14.

∗ 10 : 10 : 20 contains 10 per cent nitrogen, 10 per cent phosphorus and 20 per cent potassium.

∗ 0 : 7 : 14 contains 0 per cent nitrogen, 7 per cent phosphorus and 14 per cent potassium.

The remaining percentage is made up of other minerals. Compound fertilisers reduce the farmer's workload because they apply more than one mineral at a time.

How fertilisers are applied to crops

∗ **Broadcasting:** Fertiliser is spread onto the surface of the soil and mixed through during further cultivations.

∗ **Top dressing:** Fertiliser is spread onto a growing crop.

∗ Placing the fertiliser **in a band** alongside the seeds using a combined drill.

Fig. 11.3 A fertiliser spreader.

Pollutants produced on the farm

* Slurry.

* Silage effluent.

* Pesticides.

* Fungicides.

* Sheep dips.

* Herbicides.

* Plastic.

* Drainage water from fields with soluble fertilisers.

* Farmyard manure.

* Surface run-off from fertilised fields.

* Run-off from milking parlours.

* Oil spillages.

How these pollutants cause pollution

* Oxygen is slightly soluble in water. When organic matter enters a river or lake, aerobic bacteria and other organisms start to break it down. This action starts to use up some of the dissolved oxygen. The higher the B.O.D. of the pollutant, the more oxygen is used up; therefore, there is less oxygen for fish, which causes them to die. Also, organic matter can coat fish gills causing them to suffocate.

> **B.O.D.: BIOLOGICAL OXYGEN DEMAND**
>
> The amount of oxygen required to fully oxidise, by biological means, the organic matter in one litre of organic pollutant or water sample.

* Some pollutants may be toxic or poisonous.

* Run-off from fertilisers results in **eutrophication:** The fertilisers cause a rapid growth in the algae resulting in algal bloom. When all the nutrients are used up, the algae begins to die. Bacteria and other organisms breakdown the algae using up the oxygen.

How to prevent silage effluent causing pollution

1. Allow the grass to wilt to reduce the amount of effluent produced.

2. Collect the silage effluent and store it in underground pits.

3. Dilute the effluent with water.

4. Spread the effluent on stubble after cutting silage.

Do not spread effluent near rivers, lakes, wells, etc. Locate silos away from rivers, lakes, wells, etc.

The advantages of hedgerows on the farm

Fig. 11.4 The importance of hedgerows.

✓ Hedgerows provide shelter for farm animals.

✓ Hedgerows are a habitat for wildlife.

✓ Hedgerows are a food source for wildlife.

✓ Hedgerows provide protection for crops.

✓ Hedgerows absorb carbon dioxide from the atmosphere through photosynthesis.

✓ Hedgerows replenish oxygen again through photosynthesis.

✓ Maintaining hedgerows on the farm is a requirement of REPS.

✓ Hedgerows provide borders to land.

12 Experiments

Experiment 1: To test a leaf for starch

1. Dip the leaf in boiling water to kill it.

2. Place in a test-tube, add methylated spirits and heat it – this process removes the chlorophyll.

3. Remove the leaf and dip in cold water to soften it.

4. Cover the leaf with iodine.

   * If starch is present, the leaf turns blue/black.

   * The leaf remains brown if no starch is present.

Experiment 2: To show that light is necessary for photosynthesis

1. Destarch a potted plant by keeping it in the dark for 24 hours.

2. Attach a piece of foil across part of the leaf and sketch it.

3. Expose the plant to strong light for four hours.

4. Remove the leaf and the foil.

5. Test the leaf for starch (*see* Experiment 1).

   * The part of the leaf which was under the foil remains brown, i.e. no starch present.

   * The part that was left uncovered goes blue/black, i.e. starch is present.

Conclusion: Light is required for a plant to photosynthesise.

Experiment 3: To show that CO_2 is necessary for photosynthesis

1. Destarch two potted plants by keeping them in the dark for 24 hours.

2. Place some soda lime in a dish on the soil of one pot. Soda lime removes CO_2 from the air. Cover each plant with a plastic bag.

3. Expose both plants to strong light for four hours.

4. Remove a leaf from both plants.

5. Test the leaf for starch (*see* Experiment 1).

   * The leaf of the plant with soda lime (no CO_2) remains brown, i.e. no starch present.

   * The leaf of the plant without the soda lime (CO_2 present) goes blue/black, i.e. starch is present.

Conclusion: CO_2 is required for a plant to photosynthesise.

Experiment 4: To show that chlorophyll is necessary for photosynthesis

1. Destarch a potted variegated plant by keeping it in the dark for 24 hours.

2. Expose the plant to strong light for four hours.

3. Remove a leaf from the plant.

4. Sketch the leaf, noting the areas where chlorophyll is present.

5. Test the leaf for starch (*see* Experiment 1).

   * The part of the leaf with no chlorophyll remains brown, i.e. no starch present.

   * The part with chlorophyll goes blue/black, i.e. starch is present.

Conclusion: Chlorophyll is required for a plant to photosynthesise.

Experiment 5: To compare the number of stomata on the upper and lower surface of a leaf

1. Apply clear nail varnish to the upper and lower surface of a leaf.

2. Allow to dry.

3. Carefully peel off the layers of nail varnish.

4. Examine the layers under a microscope.

5. Count the number of bumps on the nail varnish (i.e. the stomata).

6. The lower surface has more stomata than the upper surface.

Experiment 6: To show the factors necessary for germination

1. Set up four test-tubes as follows:

    * Test-tube A (control): Moist cotton wool, seeds and place in a warm place.

    * Test-tube B: Dry cotton wool, seeds and place in a warm place.

    * Test-tube C: Moist cotton wool, seeds and place in the fridge.

    * Test-tube D: Cotton wool and seeds, fill the test-tube with water and cover with a layer of oil, place in a warm place.

2. Leave the test-tubes for 10 days.

3. Seeds in test-tube A germinated.

4. No germination occurred in test-tubes B, C and D.

Experiment 7: To show the effect of nutrient deficiency on plant growth

1. Get two sterilised test-tubes.

2. Get two seedlings of equal size.

3. Using nutrient tablets, make up two solutions.

    * One solution has all the nutrients present.

    * The other solution is missing one nutrient.

4. Fill the flasks with the solutions; add the seedlings and an aeration tube.

5. Cover both flasks with tin foil and leave for two weeks.

6. Top up the nutrient solution during the two weeks.

    * The seedling with all the nutrients grows well.

    * The second seedling shows poor growth.

NO NITROGEN

Stunted growth due to the lack of protein.

NO PHOSPHORUS

Stunted growth due to poor root formation.

NO POTASSIUM

Stunted growth due to poor protein formation.

NO MAGNESIUM

Chlorosis due to the inability to make chlorophyll.

NO CALCIUM

Stunted growth due to the lack of cell wall production.

NO IRON

Chlorosis due to the inability to make chlorophyll.

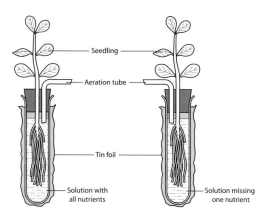

Seedling

Aeration tube

Tin foil

Solution with all nutrients

Solution missing one nutrient

AERATION TUBE

The aeration tube allows the roots to respire and produce the energy necessary for active transport.

TIN FOIL

The tin foil prevents any algae which may be present in the water from competing with the seedling for nutrients.

Fig. 12.1 The effect of nutrient deficiency on plant growth.

Experiment 8: To show that germinating seeds release energy

1. Get two lots of peas, one live and one dead.

   The **peas are killed** by boiling them in water.

2. Sterilise the seeds to prevent the growth of bacteria.

3. Place the live peas in one thermos flask and the dead peas in another; the dead peas are the control.

4. Insert a thermometer into both flasks and plug with cotton wool.

5. Record the temperature of both flasks.

6. Leave the peas for 1 week.

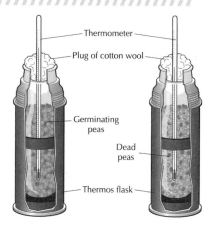

Thermometer

Plug of cotton wool

Germinating peas

Dead peas

Thermos flask

Fig. 12.2 To show that germinating seeds release energy.

7. After one week, note the temperature of the flasks.

    * The flask with the live peas had a rise in temperature.

    * There was no temperature change in the control.

Experiment 9: To demonstrate the rate of transpiration using a potometer

1. Obtain a seedling with healthy leaves.

2. Fill the potometer under water.

3. Place the seedling in the potometer.

4. Remove from the water keeping the capillary tube in the water.

5. Gently remove the capillary tube from the water and allow an air bubble to enter; return to the water.

6. Note the position of the air bubble.

7. Place in the potometer on a window sill for 3–4 hours.

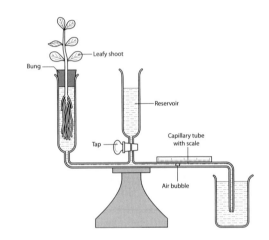

Fig. 12.3 A potometer.

8. After 3–4 hours note the position of the bubble. The bubble has moved closer to the plant.

Conclusion: Water lost through the leaves was replaced by water in the potometer. The water was lost due to transpiration.

Experiment 10: To demonstrate transpiration in a plant using a bell jar

1. Get a well-watered potted plant.

2. Cover the soil with a plastic bag.

3. Place a bell jar over the plant.

Cobalt chloride paper goes from blue to pink in the presence of water.

4. Leave in good light for 3–4 hours.

5. After 3–4 hours, note the condensation on the inside of the bell jar.

6. Prove the presence of water using cobalt chloride paper.

7. Water was lost from the surface of the plant due to transpiration.

Experiment 11: To demonstrate the transpiration stream

1. Get a stick of celery.

2. Fill a beaker with water and add a dye to it.

3. Place the celery in the dyed water for 1 hour.

4. Remove the celery from the water.

5. Examine the veins in the leaves of the celery – these have turned the colour of the dye.

6. Cut across the celery stem to examine xylem tubes. These have also turned the colour of the dye.

Experiment 12: To demonstrate the range of pigments found in a grass plant

1. Place some grass and sand in a pestle and mortar.

2. Grind up the grass leaves.

3. Add acetone to the grass.

The pigments are chlorophyll a, chlorophyll b, xanthophylls, phaeophytin and carotene.

4. Filter the mixture.

5. Place a drop of extract on chromatography paper or filter paper.

6. Place some solvent (e.g. acetone) in a covered glass jar and place the end of the paper in the solvent.

Conclusion: The pigments are separated by chromatography.

Experiment 13: To demonstrate osmosis

1. Get some Visking tubing.

2. Fill the Visking tubing with sugar solution.

3. Place the Visking tubing in a beaker of water.

4. Leave for 20 minutes.

> **Osmosis** is the movement of water from an area of high concentration to an area of low concentration.

Result: The water moves from the beaker into the Visking tubing.

Experiment 14: To demonstrate phototropism

1. Get a cardboard box and cut a hole out on one side.

2. Cover a seedling with the cardboard box.

3. Leave in good light for 2–3 days.

Result: The seedling will have grown towards the light.

Experiment 15: To demonstrate geotropism

1. Fill a glass jar with moist cotton wool.

2. Place two bean seeds between the cotton wool and glass.

3. Place one bean the right way up.

4. Place the second bean on its side.

5. Leave for one week for germination to occur.

   * The shoots grow upwards.

   * The roots grow downwards.

Experiment 16: To show the micro-propagation of plants

1. Fill a petri dish with a nutrient medium.

2. Remove a small number of cells from a plant and place in the petri dish.

3. Place the dish in good light at 20–25 °C.

4. The cells multiply and a callus forms.

5. Transfer the callus to a different medium to encourage the development of roots and shoots.

6. Plant the small plants in soil.

Experiment 17: To obtain and grow a culture of bacteria for the root nodules of a clover plant

1. Dig up a clover plant.

2. Remove the soil from the roots.

3. Rinse the roots with a disinfectant.

4. Crush the root nodules.

5. Sterilise an inoculating loop.

6. Transfer some of the bacteria using an inoculating loop.

7. Streak the bacteria onto an agar plate.

8. Incubate the agar plate for one week.

Conclusion: Colonies of Rhizobium bacteria will be seen growing on the agar plate.

Experiment 18: To assess the hygienic quality of milk

1. Sterilise four test-tubes.

2. Label the test-tubes A, B, C, D.

3. Place 10 ml of milk in each test-tube.

   * A: Fresh pasteurised milk.

   * B: Fresh unpasteurised milk.

   * C: Sour pasteurised milk.

   * D: Sour unpasteurised milk.

4. Add 1 ml of Resazurin solution to each test-tube.

5. Stopper the test-tubes and incubate at 37 °C for 10 minutes in a water bath.

6. Place the test-tubes in a test-tube rack and examine the colour of each test-tube.

   * Test-tube A: 10 ml of fresh pasteurised milk.   Blue colour

   * Test-tube B: 10 ml of fresh unpasteurised milk.   Mauve colour

   * Test-tube C: 10 ml of sour pasteurised milk.   Pink colour

   * Test-tube D: 10 ml of sour unpasteurised milk.   White colour

   Hygienic quality is indicated with colour change:

Blue	–	Mauve	–	Pink	–	White
Best quality						Poorest quality

Experiment 19: To show the presence of bacteria in a sample of milk

1. Obtain five sterile agar plates.

2. Label the agar plates A, B, C, D, E.

3. Sterilise an inoculating loop.

4. Transfer the milk sample to the agar plates using the inoculating loop.

5. Streak the milk sample onto the agar plate.

   * A: Fresh pasteurised milk.

   * B: Fresh unpasteurised milk.

   * C: Sour pasteurised milk.

   * D: Sour unpasteurised milk.

   * E: No milk (control).

6. Sterilise the loop between samples.

7. Seal each of the agar plates.

8. Incubate the agar plates for 24–48 hours.

9. Observe the presence of any bacterial colonies.

   * The number of bacterial colonies increases from plate A to D.

   * No colonies found on plate E.

Experiment 20: To determine the soil texture by sedimentation

1. Place a sample of soil in a beaker with some hot water.

2. Allow it to soak for 2–3 minutes.

3. Mix soil suspension vigorously until the soil is thoroughly broken up.

4. Pour the suspension into a graduated cylinder.

5. Cover the graduated cylinder and shake for one minute.

6. Add water to bring the solution up to the 100 ml mark.

7. Cover the graduated cylinder and invert it two or three times.

8. Place the graduated cylinder on the bench and allow to settle.

9. When settled, calculate the percentage of sand, silt and clay in the soil sample.

10. Use a soil textural triangle to determine the soil texture.

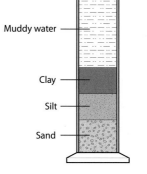

Fig. 12.4 To determine the soil texture by sedimentation.

Experiment 21: To determine the soil texture by feel

1. Get a sample of sandy soil and clay soil.

2. Examine the soil samples using a hand lens.

3. Handle the soil and note the feel of the samples.

4. Moisten the samples with a little water.

5. Note the cohesiveness and plasticity of the samples.

6. Roll the samples into threads and bend.

7. Use a table of pre-determined information to decide the soil textures.

SANDY SOIL	CLAY SOIL
• Gritty feel. • Will not stick together when wet. • Will not role into threads.	• Non-gritty feel. • Sticks together when wet. • Will role into threads and bend.

Experiment 22: To demonstrate the drainage of different soil samples

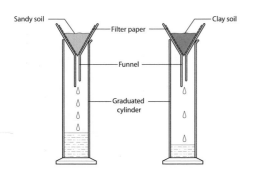

Fig. 12.5 To demonstrate the drainage of different soil samples.

1. Set up the experiment as shown.

2. Add an equal amount of soil to each funnel.

3. Add equal volumes of water to each soil.

4. Measure the length of time it takes for water to drain through.

5. Sandy soils have better drainage than clay soils.

Experiment 23: To demonstrate soil capillarity

1. Get two open-ended glass tubes.

2. Fill one with sand and the other with clay.

3. Plug the ends of the tubes with cotton wool.

4. Place both tubes in a beaker of water.

5. Leave for a number of hours.

6. Observe the movement of water up through the glass tubes.

   * Water moves up through the clay soil.

   * Very little water movement in the sand sample.

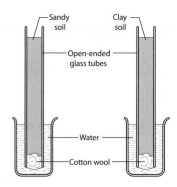

Fig. 12.6 To demonstrate soil capillarity.

Experiment 24: To demonstrate the role of earthworms in the soil

1. Set up a wormery using different types of material.

2. Place clay, gravel, sand, lime and leaves in layers in the wormery.

3. Add worms and cover.

4. Set up a wormery with no worms as a control.

5. Leave the wormeries in a dark, cool place for one week.

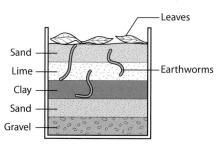

Fig. 12.7 A wormery.

6. Observe the changes in the wormeries after one week.

* The layers are mixed up.

* The worms bring the leaves down from the surface.

* Channels are produced by the movement of the worms.

* There is no change in the control.

Experiment 25: To determine the number of earthworms present in a soil

1. Measure a 1m² area in a grassland area.

2. Remove all vegetation from the area using a shears.

3. Make up a solution of washing up liquid and water.

4. Apply the solution to the area.

5. The earthworms will now come to the surface of the soil.

6. Count the number of earthworms.

Experiment 26: To determine the organic matter and inorganic matter content of a soil

1. Weigh a dried sample of soil.

2. Place in a crucible over a Bunsen burner.

3. Black smoke will start to come from the soil.

> The **black smoke** is the organic matter (humus) being burnt off.

4. Heat until the soil particles glow red.

5. Reweigh soil sample.

* Loss in weight equals the organic matter content.

* Soil remaining is equal to the inorganic matter content.

Percentage of organic matter content $= \dfrac{\text{loss in weight}}{\text{weight of sample}} \times 100$

Percentage of inorganic matter content $= \dfrac{\text{weight remaining}}{\text{weight of sample}} \times 100$

Experiment 27: To determine the percentage dry matter and percentage water in a soil

1. Weigh the container.

2. Weigh the soil sample and container.

3. Calculate the weight of the soil sample.

4. Place the sample in an oven at 100 °C.

5. Remove the sample and weigh it.

6. Replace it in the oven.

7. Remove it again and weigh it.

8. Repeat steps 5, 6 and 7 until the weight of the sample remains constant.

9. Calculate the percentage of water and the percentage of dry matter in the sample.

$$\text{Percentage water} = \frac{\text{loss in weight}}{\text{weight of sample}} \times 100$$

$$\text{Percentage dry matter content} = \frac{\text{weight remaining}}{\text{weight of sample}} \times 100$$

Experiment 28: To determine the temperature of soil

1. Dig a hole in the soil.

2. Coat the bulb of a thermometer with many layers of wax.

3. Place the thermometer in the ground.

4. Leave there for 2–3 hours.

5. Remove the thermometer and read the temperature.

> **Covering the bulb with wax** prevents the atmospheric temperature from affecting the temperature before the read is taken.

Experiment 29: To determine the percentage of air in a soil

1. Get an empty can.

2. Measure the volume of the can.

3. Insert the can in the ground.

4. Remove the can and soil sample.

5. Add a known volume of water to a graduated cylinder.

6. Pour the water into the soil sample until the can is full.

7. Measure the amount of water added.

8. The volume of the water added is equal to the amount of air in the soil.

9. Calculate the percentage of air in the soil. Ideally, the percentage of air should be about 25 per cent.

Experiment 30: To determine the pH of a soil

1. Place a small quantity of soil in a beaker.

2. Add a small quantity of water to the beaker, stir the solution and allow to stand for 10 minutes.

3. Insert the electrode of a pH meter into the soil solution.

4. Record the pH of the soil.

Experiment 31: To demonstrate Cation Exchange Capacity (CEC)

1. Obtain a small sample of a soil with a high pH.

2. Place filter paper in a funnel and add the soil sample.

3. Slowly add potassium chloride reagent.

4. Test the leachate for calcium by adding ammonium oxalate reagent.

5. White precipitate indicates appositive result.

6. Continue adding the potassium chloride and testing the leachate.

7. Continue testing for calcium until the test is negative.

Conclusion: The soil colloids have been transformed from being calcium dominated to potassium dominated.

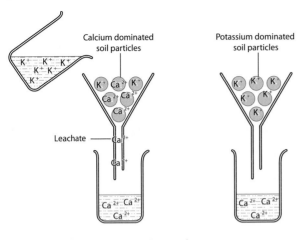

A **recently limed soil** will have a high pH and will be calcium dominated.

Fig. 12.8 To demonstrate Cation Exchange Capacity (CEC).

Experiment 32: To demonstrate soil flocculation

1. Make up a suspension of clay by adding a handful of clay to water and shake well.

2. Divide the solution between three graduated cylinders.

3. Label the cylinders A, B and C.

4. To A, add calcium chloride or limewater.

5. To B, add sodium hydroxide or sodium bicarbonate.

6. To C, add water.

7. Mix well and allow to settle.

   * The soil flocculates in cylinder A.

   * No flocculation occurs in cylinders B and C.

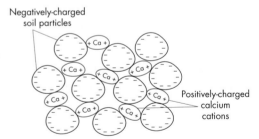

Fig. 12.9 To demonstrate soil flocculation.

Conclusion: Calcium cations are required for flocculation to occur.

The **calcium cations** act like a 'bridge' between the soil particles and stick them together. These soil clusters then sink to the bottom of the cylinder.

Experiment 33: To determine the lime requirement of soil

1. Get six small screw cap bottles.

2. Add 10 g of soil to each bottle.

3. Add calcium hydroxide to each bottle.

   * Bottle 1: 0 g of calcium hydroxide.

   * Bottle 2: 0.01 g of calcium hydroxide.

   * Bottle 3: 0.02 g of calcium hydroxide.

   * Bottle 4: 0.04 g of calcium hydroxide.

   * Bottle 5: 0.08 g of calcium hydroxide.

   * Bottle 6: 0.16 g of calcium hydroxide.

> The **lime requirement** of a soil is the amount of lime required to increase the pH of the soil up to 6.5.

4. Add 25 ml of water and two drops of chloroform to each bottle.

5. Close the bottles and shake.

6. Leave for one week.

7. After one week, take the pH of each bottle using a pH meter.

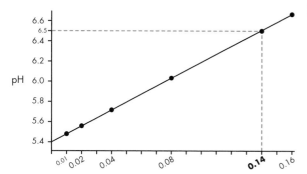

Lime required in tonnes/ha:

$$\frac{X \times 100 \times 227}{74}$$

Fig. 12.10 A graph of the pH versus calcium hydroxide added.

> **X:** Read from the graph.
> **100:** Molecular weight of calcium carbonate.
> **74:** Molecular weight of calcium hydroxide.
> **227:** Converts g/10g to tonnes/ha.

Experiment 34: To obtain a sample of soil for soil testing

1. Collect 20–25 soil samples from the field being tested. Areas to avoid are around feeding and water troughs, marsh areas, the headlands, gateways and pathways.

2. Collect the samples in the shape of a W.

3. Place all the samples in one bag and send off for testing.

Experiment 35: To investigate the presence of minerals in a soil

1. Place a sample of soil in a conical flask.

2. Add distilled water.

3. Stopper and shake.

4. Filter the contents of the flask.

5. Add a few drops of the correct reagent to the filtrate.

6. State the result.

WHEN TESTING FOR NITROGEN
Add diphenylamine reagent.
Blue precipitate indicates a positive result.

WHEN TESTING FOR CALCIUM
Add ammonium oxalate reagent.
White precipitate indicates a positive result.

WHEN TESTING FOR PHOSPHORUS
Add ammonium molybdate reagent.
Yellow precipitate indicates a positive result.

WHEN TESTING FOR SULPHATES
Add barium chloride reagent.
White cloudiness indicates a positive result.

WHEN TESTING FOR CHLORIDES
Add silver nitrate reagent.
White precipitate indicates a positive result.

Experiment 36: To determine the botanical composition of an area

1. Use a line transect and a quadrat.

2. Throw the quadrat randomly.

3. Place the line transect.

4. Using a key, identify the different plant species.

5. Note the frequency of each plant species.

6. Estimate the percentage cover of each plant species.

Experiment 37: To investigate the protein content in a sample of grass

1. Weigh the sample of grass.

2. Separate the leaf from the stem.

3. Weigh each lot separately.

4. Calculate the leaf to stem ratio. The ratio is proportional to the protein content of the grass.

> At the **leafy stage**, grass contains more than 15 per cent **protein**.
> At the **stemmy stage**, the protein content falls to less the 12 per cent.

OR

1. Use the Kjeildahl method to detect the nitrogen content.

   * Protein contains 16 per cent nitrogen.

   * The percentage of protein is equal to the percentage of N × by 100/16

Experiment 38: To investigate the productivity of an area of grassland

1. Measure an area of grassland.

2. Enclose the area and mow the grass.

3. Weigh the amount of grass removed and record it.

4. Repeat this once a week for one year.

5. The total weight of grass removed is a measure of productivity.

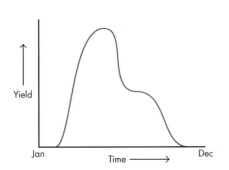

> **GRASS GROWTH CURVE**
> The weight of grass removed is plotted against time

Fig. 12.11 The grass growth curve.

Experiment 39: To investigate the influence of the element nitrogen on grass growth

1. Mow an area of grass.
2. Mark out five 1 m² areas.
    *   To area 1, add 0 g of nitrogen.
    *   To area 2, add 25 g of nitrogen.
    *   To area 3, add 50 g of nitrogen.
    *   To area 4, add 75 g of nitrogen.
    *   To area 5, add 100 g of nitrogen.
3. Record the height of the grass in the five areas throughout the growing season.

Experiment 40: To determine the percentage of soluble carbohydrates in a sample of grass

1. Dry a sample of grass and place in a plastic bag.
2. Roll the bag to remove the air and place in a freezer until frozen.
3. Remove from the freezer; at this stage, the cells have burst releasing the cell sap.
4. Squeeze out a drop and place on a refractometer.
5. Obtain a reading along with two further readings from other drops.
6. Calculate the mean reading and estimate the percentage of soluble carbohydrates.

7. Knowing the carbohydrate content will allow you to estimate the amount of additive required.

> The percentage of water soluble carbohydrates (**WSC**) in grass juice is 1–5 per cent. Grass with a WSC of greater than 3 per cent does not require an additive at silage making. Dry weather and sunshine increases the WSC of grass.

Experiment 42: To identify the differences in silage quality

1. Find a newly opened silage pit and note the texture colour and smell of the silage.

	LACTIC ACID	BUTYRIC ACID	OVERHEATED
TEXTURE	Firm	Slimy	Dryish
COLOUR	Light yellowish green	Dark green	Brown/black
SMELL	Sharp and vinegary	Unpleasant, rancid	Sweet like burnt sugar

2. Water/dry matter content: Squeeze sample in one hand OR wring using two hands.

   * If liquid can be squeezed out using one hand => poor quality

   ($<$20 per cent DM).

   * If liquid can be wrung out using two hands => good quality

   (20–25 per cent DM).

   * If liquid cannot be removed by hand => very good quality

   ($>$25 per cent DM).

3. pH: Touch the samples with the tip of your tongue OR squeeze out sufficient liquid to measure using a pH meter.

   * If sample is not sharp to tongue – pH > 5 => Butyric acid silage.
   * If sample is sharply acid to tongue – pH < 5 => Lactic acid silage.

Experiment 43: To determine the percentage germination of a sample of seeds

1. Place a layer of cotton wool on a seed tray.

2. Place 100 seeds on the tray.

3. Moisten the cotton wool.

4. Ensure the temperature is suitable (room temperature).

5. Leave for 10–14 days (depending on the seeds used).

6. Count the number of seeds germinated, i.e. the number which has sprouted.

7. Repeat experiment two more times.

8. Get the average.

9. Work out the percentage germination.

> If using Certified Seed, the percentage **germination** should be greater than 85 per cent.

Experiment 44: To determine the percentage purity of a sample of barley seeds

1. Weigh out 100 g of seed.

2. Sift through the seeds and remove anything that is not a barley seed, e.g. weed seeds, other seeds, dust, pieces of straw.

3. Repeat this with two other lots of seed.

4. Reweigh each sample and find the average.

5. Calculate the percentage purity of the sample of barley seeds.

> If using Certified Seed, the percentage **purity** should be greater than 98 per cent.

Experiment 45: To estimate the yield of a crop prior to harvesting

1. Locate a crop ready for harvesting.

2. Using a quadrat, measure a $1m^2$ area.

3. Remove the crop.

4. Remove the tops or remove the seeds from the seed head.

5. Weigh the root or grain.

6. Record the result.

7. Repeat three times.

8. Calculate the average weight per area.

9. Calculate the yield per hectare.

10. State the correct expected yield.

> **BARLEY**
> Winter barley: 7–8 ton/ha.
> Spring barley: ≈ 5 ton/ha.
>
> **POTATOES**
> First earlies: 7–10 ton/ha.
> Main crop: 30–40 ton/ha.
>
> **SUGARBEET**
> Roots: 40 ton/ha.
> Tops: 25–30 ton/ha.

Experiment 46: To demonstrate the presence of fat in a food sample

1. Obtain two pieces of brown paper.

2. Rub the food sample (milk, butter, oil, etc.) onto the first piece of paper.

> A **translucent spot** indicates the presence of fats.

3. Put a drop of water on the second piece of paper – this is the control.

4. Allow both pieces of paper to dry.

   * The first piece of paper will have a translucent spot.

   * There will be no translucent spot on the control.

Experiment 47: To demonstrate the presence of protein in a food sample (Biuret test)

1. Get two test-tubes.

2. Add the food sample (milk, egg white, peas, etc.) to test-tube A.

3. If the food is solid, grind it up with a little water and filter the mixture.

4. Add water to test-tube B.

5. Add sodium hydroxide and copper sulphate to both test-tubes.

6. Gently shake both test-tubes.

   * Test-tube A turns purple indicating the presence of protein.

   > Positive result = purple.
   > Negative result = blue.

   * Test-tube B will remain blue.

Experiment 48: To demonstrate the presence of glucose

1. To test-tube A, add some glucose solution.

2. Add water to test-tube B.

3. Add Benedict's solution to both test-tubes.

4. Place both test-tubes in a water bath and heat gently.

   * Test-tube A turns brick red indicating the presence of glucose.

   * Test-tube B will remain blue.

> Positive result = brick red.
> Negative result = blue.

Experiment 49: To demonstrate the presence of sucrose

1. Place a drop of the food sample on a refractometer.

2. Read the percentage sugar present.

3. Add a drop of water on the refractometer as a control. Percentage sugar present is zero.

Experiment 50: To demonstrate the presence of vitamin C

1. Add orange juice to test-tube A.

2. Add water to test-tube B.

3. Add DCPIP solution to both test-tubes.

   * Test-tube A will turn back to the colour of the juice, i.e. orange.

   * Test-tube B will remain blue.

> **DCPIP** is blue in colour. It goes colourless in the presence of Vitamin C.

Experiment 51: The percentage of water and solids in a sample of milk

1. Weigh the container.

2. Weigh the milk sample and container.

3. Calculate the weight of the milk sample.

4. Place in the oven at 100 °C until all the water evaporates.

5. Remove from the oven and weigh again.

6. Calculate the loss in weight.

7. The weight lost is equal to the water content.

8. Calculate the percentage of water and solids in the sample.

$$\text{Percentage of water} = \frac{\text{loss in weight}}{\text{weight of sample}} \times 100$$

$$\text{Percentage of solids} = \frac{\text{loss in weight}}{\text{weight of sample}} \times 100$$

MILK
Percentage water: 87.5 %
Percentage solids: 12.5 %
COLOSTRUM
Percentage water: 78 %
Percentage solids: 22 %

Experiment 52: To demonstrate the presence of micro-organisms in an animal foodstuff

1. Get a sample of foodstuff.

2. Get two sterile agar plates.

3. Keep one plate unopened; this is the control.

4. Flame an inoculating loop.

5. Transfer a sample of the foodstuff to the agar plate using an inoculating loop.

6. Incubate the plate upside down.

7. Leave for 24–48 hours.

   * Furry growth on the agar indicates the presence of fungus.

   * Dome-shaped colonies indicate the presence of bacteria.

   * The control remains clear.

FOODSTUFFS
Milk.
Concentrates.
Silage.
Hay.

Experiment 53: To investigate the effect of salivary amylase on starch

(To show the action of a named enzyme)

1. Make up two test-tubes of starch solution (dissolve the starch powder in warm water); label the test-tubes A and B.

2. Rinse your mouth with water and collect the saliva in a test-tube.

3. Add the saliva to test-tube A.

4. Place test-tubes A and B in the water bath at 37 °C.

5. After two minutes, remove the test-tubes and add iodine to both.

   ✱ Test-tube A: Iodine remained brown – the salivary amylase had digested the starch.

   ✱ Test-tube B: Iodine turned blue/black – the starch was still present.

Experiment 54: To demonstrate that food contains energy

1. Obtain a high energy food, e.g. oil, sugar, peanuts.

2. Put 100 cm^3 of water into a beaker and note the temperature.

3. Heat the food until it starts to burn.

4. Place the burning food under the beaker of water.

5. Leave there until the food is completely burned.

6. Note the final temperature of the water.

> **Heat** is a form of energy.

Conclusion: The increase in temperature is due to the energy released from the food.

Glossary

A

Aberdeen Angus: A British beef breed.

Abomasum: The fourth chamber in the stomach of a ruminant.

Acid leaching: When the water percolating through the soil is acidic.

Acid treatment: A method of storing barley for up to a period of 6 months.

Aerobic respiration: Oxygen is required; glucose is completely broken down to CO_2 and H_2O; a large amount of energy is released.

Agar: A jelly-like substance used to grow bacteria in the laboratory.

Aggressive grass: A grass that tillers vigorously.

Altitude: The height above ground level.

Anabolism: Constructive metabolism; the synthesis in living organisms of more complex substances from simpler ones, e.g. photosynthesis.

Anaerobic respiration: Also referred to as fermentation. The incomplete breakdown of glucose; in the absence of oxygen.

Awns: The hairs found on the seeds of some plants, e.g. barley and Italian ryegrass.

B

Backcross: Used to determine whether an organism is heterozygous or homozygous dominant. The unknown is crossed with a homozygous recessive organism.

Basalt: An igneous rock formed by the quick cooling of magma on the earth's surface.

Beef weanlings: In suckler beef farming, when the calves are separated from their mother, they are referred to as beef weanlings.

Belclare improver: A breed of sheep that has been developed by crossing the Galway with the Finish Landrace (to improve prolifacy) and the Llynn (to improve conformation).

Bile duct: Bile (formed in the liver and stored in the gall bladder) enters the small intestine via the bile duct.

Binary fission: A method of asexual reproduction that involves the splitting of a parent cell into two approximately equal parts.

Biological pest control: The control of one organism by the deliberate use of another organism.

Blackface Mountain: A mountain breed of sheep. They are small, very hardy and able to withstand mountain conditions.

Botanical composition: The variety of plants in an area.

Bowman's capsule: Located at the top of each nephron, in the kidney.

Bradford count: The number of hanks of yarn, each 520 m long that can be spun from 450 g of wool prepared for spinning. It is a measure of wool quality.

Brassica: Any plant belonging to the genus Brassica, including many important vegetables, such as cabbage, kale, rape, broccoli, cauliflower, turnip and mustard.

C

Caecum: A part of the large intestine.

Canine: The teeth used for tearing food.

Carpals: The bones in the wrist.

Catabolism: Destructive metabolism; the breaking down in living organisms of more complex substances into simpler ones, with the release of energy, e.g. respiration.

Cell organelles: A structure within a cell, such as a vacuole, that performs a specific function.

Cerebellum: Above the medulla oblongata and below the cerebrum; controls balance and muscle activity.

Cerebrum: The forebrain and the midbrain; controls voluntary movements and coordinates mental actions. The pituitary gland is located here.

Cervix: The neck of the uterus (womb).

Charolais: Continental beef breed; produces large amounts of lean meat.

Chlorosis: The breakdown of chlorophyll in a plant.

Clinostat: An apparatus consisting of a slowly revolving disk which eliminates the effects of gravity.

Clones: Organisms which have the exact same genotype.

Clostridium: Bacteria involved in the production of butyric acid silage.

Club root: Fungus disease of turnips, cabbages and cauliflower; it is controlled by crop rotation.

Cocksfoot: A grass suitable for light sandy soils, but will become unpalatable if under grazed.

Colostrum (also known as beastings): The first milk produced after an animal gives birth.

Concentrates: A high-energy food fed to animals.

Conception: The fertilisation of the egg.

Creep gate: The gate used in creep grazing; the young animals can move through the gate.

Crossing over: The exchange of genes from one chromosome to another; occurs during cell division.

Crucible: A dish used when heating materials to high temperatures.

Crude protein: The total amount of protein in a food.

D

Diaphragm: One of the main muscles involved in breathing.

Diffusion: The movement of particles from a region of high concentration to a region of low concentration.

Disaccharides: When two simple sugars are joined together, e.g. sucrose and lactose.

Dormancy: When all metabolic activity is reduced; normal activity resumes when conditions are favourable.

Double chop harvester: Used to cut grass when saving it as silage; the grass is cut into small pieces.

Dry sow house: The house where the sow is kept after her bonhams have been weaned and before she gives birth to her next litter.

E

Ectoparasite: a parasite that lives on the outside of its host.

Egestion: The removal of undigested and unabsorbed food from the body.

Endoparasite: a parasite that lives within its host.

Endoskeleton: An internal skeleton or framework.

Endosperm seed: A seed which has some of its food reserve contained within a special tissue called the endosperm and also in the cotyledon.

Excretion: Getting rid of the waste products of metabolism.

Exoskeleton: A hard outer covering that provides protection and support.

Exoparasite: A parasite that lives on the outside of its host.

F

Fallopian tubes: The egg travels along the fallopian tube from the ovary to the uterus (womb).

Farrowing crate: The sow is held in this small area from one week before she gives birth until her bonhams are weaned.

Farrowing house: The house where the sow gives birth.

Fasiola hepatica: Commonly called the liverfluke.

Fattener house: The house where young pigs are kept in the weeks prior to slaughter.

First earlies: Potatoes that can be planted as early as February and harvested from May.

Flocculation: Clay particles come together into floccules or small clusters and improve soil structure.

Florets: Some flowers are made up of a collection of small flowers called florets.

Foster crate: Used in sheep farming to encourage a ewe to foster a lamb.

Friesian: In addition to its high milk yields, it supplies calves for the beef industry.

FYM (farmyard manure): A by-product of winter housing of animals. It is a mixture of faeces, urine and bedding which has rotted during storage.

G

Gley soil: Wet and poorly structured soils. They have a short growing season but where drainage can be successfully carried out, their potential may be improved considerably.

Glycogen: In the animal's body; excess carbohydrates are converted to glycogen and stored.

Granite: An igneous rock formed by the slow cooling of magma, beneath the earth's surface.

Greening: Occurs when potatoes are exposed to sunlight.

H

Holstein: A pure dairy breed; similar in appearance to Friesian but are taller and of lighter confirmation.

Hydroponics: The cultivation of plants in a nutrient solution (water) rather than soil.

Hydroskeleton: A fluid-filled cavity that functions as a skeleton.

I

Incisor: The front teeth, they are used for cutting food.

Inflorescence: A number of flowers together on a branched stem.

Inoculating loop: An instrument used to transfer a sample of bacteria.

Iron pan: Found in the subsoil of some soils. It is a layer which is impervious to water.

L

Lactation: The secretion of milk from the udder of an animal.

Lactation curve: A graph of the variation in the milk yields over the lactation period.

Lactation peak: The day the highest milk yield is produced, usually day 70.

Lactation period: The length of time an animal produces milk.

Lactation yield: The amount of milk produced in one lactation.

Lactose: The sugar found in milk.

Lichen: A fungus and an alga growing together in a symbiotic relationship.

Limewater: Used to test for the presence of carbon dioxide.

Limousin: A beef breed, light-boned with the ability to put on masses of lean meat.

Livestock unit (LU): The amount of farm livestock which consumes a quantity of food equivalent to that consumed by a mature productive cow.

Locus: The position of a gene on a chromosome.

Lodging: The collapse of all or part of a crop, usually caused by the straw being too tall, too weak, diseased or the crop being overly fertilised by nitrogen.

Loop of Henle: The long U-shaped part of the nephron.

M

Maintenance feeding: The feed requirements of an animal to maintain their current body weight and state of health.

Masster muscle: A muscle in the cheek that opens and closes the jaws during chewing.

Medulla: The outermost part of the kidney.

Mendel's 1st law (law of segregation): Characteristics are controlled by pairs of factors (genes) which segregate during gamete formation and are restored at fertilisation.

Mendel's 2nd law (law of independent assortment): When gametes are formed, either of a pair of alleles is equally likely to combine with either of another pair of alleles.

Metabolic disorder: Diseases associated with high levels of production, e.g. twin lamb disease, milk fever.

Metamorphic rock: Are formed by the action of intense heat or pressure on igneous or sedimentary rocks, e.g. marble, quartzite.

Milch cows: A cow kept or suitable for milk production.

Milking off her back: The cow uses some of her stored energy to produce colostrum or milk in the first few days after calving.

Mineral: Inorganic substances required by plants and animals for normal growth.

Mitochondria: Aerobic respiration occurs in these cell organelles.

Molar: The back teeth; they are used for chewing food.

Monosaccharide: The simplest form of carbohydrates, e.g. glucose, galactose and fructose.

Mulch: A protective covering, placed around plants to prevent the evaporation of moisture, the freezing of roots and/or the growth of weeds.

Multiple alleles: When more than two alleles control a trait, e.g. the blood.

N

Nectar: A sweet liquid secreted by flowers.

Nematodes: Members of the phylum nematoda.

Nephron: There are about a million of these in each kidney. The nephron filters waste products from the blood and regulates the water/salt balance in the body.

O

Obligate parasite: Parasites that cannot survive without a host.

P

Palatability: Agreeable to taste.

Phytophora infestans: Commonly called the potato blight.

Plumule: The first shoot of a seedling.

Polyploidy: A cell containing multiple copies of chromosomes.

Polysaccharide: Complex carbohydrates, e.g. starch, glycogen, cellulose and chitin.

Pregnancy Toxemia (also known as 'twin lamb disease'): A disease which may affect pregnant ewes.

Premolar: The back teeth; they are used for chewing food.

Production feeding: The feed requirements of an animal to produce milk, an unborn animal and/or meat.

Progeny: The offspring.

Prolific: Producing offspring or fruit in abundance.

Pulmonary artery: The artery that takes deoxygenated blood from the heart to the lungs.

Pulmonary vein: The vein that brings oxygenated blood from the lungs to the heart.

R

Radicle: The first root of a seedling.

Radius: One of the bones that run from the elbow to the wrist.

Records: A variety of potato which is fairly resistant to tuber blight.

Renal artery: The artery that brings blood containing wastes and oxygen to the kidneys.

REPS: Rural Environmental Protection Scheme.

Residue borne disease: A disease that is able to survive in the remains of a crop after harvesting and will go on to infect the next crop unless crop rotation is practised.

Root mat: The layer of fibrous roots produced by grass plants.

Rumen: One of the chambers in the stomach of a ruminant animal.

S

Saprophyte: An organism that grows on and gets its nourishment from dead or decaying organic matter.

Scrub: A large area covered with low trees and shrubs.

Septum: The septum divides the heart in two and prevents oxygenated and deoxygenated blood from mixing.

Sex chromosomes: The chromosomes which determine whether animals are male or female; males are XY and females are XX.

Sex linkage: The genes are located on the sex chromosomes.

Slurry seeding: When grass seeds are either mixed with slurry and spread on the pasture; or the seed is spread first and the slurry applied after.

Soil auger: The instrument used to extract a sample of a soil profile.

Soil colloids: Chemically active constituents in the soil.

Split dressings: Refers to applying nitrogen fertiliser. Some of the nitrogen is applied in early spring and the remainder later in the spring.

Strip milking: Draws of milk are removed per teat; this milk helps identify clinical mastitis and other abnormalities.

Stubble: The part of the crop which remains in the field after the crop has been harvested.

Subcutaneous fat: The layer of fat lying underneath the skin.

Suckler beef: This is when the calves are reared by their mothers. The calves suckle their mother from birth to weaning.

Sward: A field of grass.

Symbiotic relationship: Two organisms living in close association and both parties benefit.

T

Tillage: Land that is ploughed and crops are sown.

Tiller: A side shoot that grows from the base of the main stem of a grass or cereal.

Tillering: The ability of grasses and cereals to form numerous side shoots from a main shoot, each growing into an individual plant.

Tilth: The physical condition of the soil relating to its suitability for growing crops.

Timothy grass: An excellent grass for hay and silage but also good for grazing. It thrives on wetter soils.

Trocar and cannula: The instrument used to treat an animal with bloat.

Turgidity: When the vacuole in a plant cell is full of liquid pushing on the cell wall.

U

Ulna: One of the bones that run from the elbow to the wrist.

Ureter: The tubes connecting the kidneys to the bladder.

Urethra: Urine leaves the bladder through the urethra.

Uterus (womb): The fertilised egg is embedded in the wall of the uterus and develops here until the young is born.

V

Vena cava: The main vein that brings deoxygenated blood back to the heart.

Ventricles: The two lower chambers in the heart.

Vertebrae: The bones that form the spinal column.

Visking tubing: Similar to the cell membrane in that it is semi-permeable.

W

Weaner house: The house in which young pigs are kept, in the weeks after being weaned.

Y

Yearlings: Animals that are one year old.

Z

Zoonose: A disease that can be transmitted from infected animals to humans.

Zoospores: A motile, flagellated asexual spore; a method of reproduction by fungi.

Zygote: During fertilisation a male and female gamete unite to form a zygote.

The Agricultural Science Examination

The exam paper is worth 300 marks (75 per cent). The project is worth 100 marks (25 per cent).

Exam paper (HL)

Structure

There are ten questions on the exam paper and you are required to do six.

QUESTION 1 has ten short questions and you are required to do six. Each question is worth 10 marks, so there is a total of 60 marks for this question.

- ✓ Attempt as many of these questions as you can and you will be rewarded the marks for the six best.
- ✓ Question 1 is not compulsory but if you don't attempt it, you will be automatically down 12 marks (3 per cent). This is because every other question on the paper is only worth 48 marks.

QUESTION 2 always focuses on the soil section of the course and is worth 48 marks. Quite often in this question, you may be asked to describe one of the soil experiments.

QUESTION 3 has two options: option one and option two. These questions can be based on any aspect of the agricultural science course. Each option is worth 48 marks. Only attempt one of these options, if you do both of them, you will only get the marks for the best one.

QUESTION 4 is the experiment question. You are given the titles of four experiments and have to describe a laboratory or field experiment for any two of them. This question is worth 48 marks.

- ✓ The main reason students do poorly in this question is that they write out the wrong experiment. Make sure you fully understand the experiment being asked.

QUESTION 5 can be based on any aspect of the agricultural science course and is worth 48 marks.

QUESTION 6 can be based on any aspect of the agricultural science course and is worth 48 marks.

QUESTION 7 always focuses on the genetics section of the course and is worth 48 marks.

✓ You will be required to carry out a genetic cross.

✓ You also need to know all the genetic definitions.

QUESTION 8 can be based on any aspect of the agricultural science course and is worth 48 marks.

✓ You are required to answer two out of three parts; each part is therefore worth 24 marks.

QUESTION 9 requires you to give a scientific explanation for four of the five statements. This question is worth 48 marks.

✓ You must state two or three points on why the given statement is true.

✓ This is one of the more popular questions on the paper but tends to be poorly answered.

Timing

Total time: 2.5 hours altogether.

Pre-start time: 10 minutes spent at the start to read all questions carefully.

Per question time: 22 minutes spent doing each question.

Post-finish time: 8 minutes spent at the end to re-read the questions and your answers.

The marking scheme

In Question 1, the amount of information is usually indicated in the question, e.g. give two reasons, state the function of each of the following, etc.

The long questions are generally divided up into parts a, b and c. Each part is usually worth 16 marks (this is not always the case though). In most questions four marks are given for each correct point, therefore you require four correct points to gain the full sixteen marks. To compensate for any change that may occur in the marking scheme, try to give five or if possible six points per part.

Previous years' topics and their corresponding questions

	2007	2006	2005	2004	2003	2002
DAIRY	6a and c	3c; 6b; 8a	3b; 6c; 4b	3b and c; 4d	3c; 8c	3a and b; 5a
BEEF	6b	6c	3c; 6a	6b and c		5c
PIGS			6b	3a	3a	5b; 8a
SHEEP	3a,b and c	8b	6b; 8a		3c	
BARLEY	3b,c; 4b	5c and d; 8c	3a,b and c		6a and b	3a,b and c
SUGARBEET	3a			4c; 8b		4d
POTATOES	3a	3a; 3b		4c; 8b and c		
ANIMAL PHYSIOLOGY	4d; 8a	3a; 4c	3a; 4c	8a	4a; 4d; 5a,b,c and d	
PLANT PHYSIOLOGY		3b; 4d	4d	3a,b and c		4c
GRASSLAND	4c; 5a,b,c and d	3c; 5a and b; 4b; 6a	5a,b and c; 8c	4b; 5a,b and c; 6a	3b; 4c; 3a and b	3c; 4a; 6a,b and c; 8b
SOIL AND FERTILISERS	4a; 8b and c	4a	4a; 8b,	4a	4b; 8a and b	4b; 8c

Points to remember

✓ The short questions and scientific explanations may be based on any aspect of the syllabus.

✓ **Question 2 has always been on soil.**

✓ **Question 7 has always been on genetics.**

Project (HL and OL)

Identification

Identification of some common plants associated with agriculture.　　10 marks

- ✓ Crops, some grasses and weeds.
- ✓ State their importance and the family they belong to.

Identification of some common animals associated with agriculture.　　10 marks

- ✓ Cattle, sheep, pigs and pests.
- ✓ State their importance and the phylum they belong to.

Experience

Crops　　15 marks

Write on at least two of the following crops

- ✓ A cereal crop.
- ✓ A root crop.
- ✓ Grassland.

Suggested headings

- ✓ Varieties.
- ✓ Place in rotation.
- ✓ Cultivation practices.
- ✓ Establishment of the crop.
- ✓ Harvesting the crop.
- ✓ Storing the crop.
- ✓ Expected yield.
- ✓ Livestock.

Farm animals　　15 marks

Write a report on a farm animal

Suggested headings

- ✓ Type of enterprise.
- ✓ Breeds.
- ✓ Husbandry.

✓ Disease control.

✓ Housing.

Farm and land layout
5 marks

✓ Farmyard layout.

✓ Layout of land.